Sharon Marshall was born in Lancashire in 1971. After completing her journalism training, she moved to London with no job and very little money, determined to make it in tabloids. Eventually, she was taken on by a national newspaper and worked as a reporter for ten years. She later became a columnist for the *Sun*, with her humorous take on single life, 'No Sex in the City'. She has worked as a TV reporter for ITV1's *This Morning* since 2003. Her first book, *The Naughty Girl's Guide to Life*, was co-authored with Tara Palmer-Tomkinson and published in 2007.

In 2008 she was made a Fellow of Blackburn College – the place that originally trained her for the madness of the media world.

Also by Sharon Marshall

The Naughty Girl's Guide to Life

With Tara Palmer-Tomkinson

TABLOID GIRL

SHARON MARSHALL

sphere

SPHERE

First published in Great Britain in 2010 by Sphere

A CIP catalogue record for this book
is available from the British Library.

ISBN 978-0-7515-4400-8

Typeset in Melior by M Rules
Printed and bound in Great Britain by
Clays Ltd, St Ives plc

Papers used by Sphere are natural, renewable and
recyclable products sourced from well-managed forests and certified
in accordance with the rules of the Forest Stewardship Council.

Mixed Sources
Product group from well-managed
forests and other controlled sources
www.fsc.org Cert no. SGS-COC-004081
FSC © 1996 Forest Stewardship Council

Sphere
An imprint of
Little, Brown Book Group
100 Victoria Embankment
London EC4Y 0DY

An Hachette UK Company
www.hachette.co.uk

www.littlebrown.co.uk

To Bruce W. Davidson

CONTENTS

This is what happened when I worked in the tabloid press. Look back through the newspaper archives and you'll see my name on these stories. I wrote them. They're true.

I'm not proud of everything we did, but I loved the tabloid journalists I worked with. Every single double-crossing, devious, scheming, cunning, ruthless, messed up, brilliantly evil one of them. And it would be a shame if they got divorced or sued as a result of this book. So that's the bit of the truth that I've fiddled with. My bit of top-spin. I worked on seven tabloid titles over a decade, which I've merged here into one newspaper. I've changed timings. I've moved dates to disguise identities. I worked with dozens of journalists, but here I've amalgamated their triumphs and their dirty deeds into a handful of characters. But rest assured, these stories all happened. These Very Bad Things were done. They still are being done. By tabloid journalists, right now.

Maybe what I did was wrong. But don't you just love to know the scandal? Don't you just love a tabloid tale?

FOREWORD

His hands descended onto my shoulders. 'No. No,' he said, and began to frogmarch me down his garden path.

My heels flailed against the gravel as I was shunted down the driveway. This was my first ever celebrity interview. It wasn't going well. In fact, I was being forcibly ejected from the property.

But a tabloid journalist never gives up. I had to get an answer. I'd get fired if I came back *without* an answer. I held the tape recorder aloft, stubbornly dug in my heels and tried once more, raising my voice over the snarls of, 'Go away.'

'Mr Jeremy Paxman,' I said, for the fourteenth time. 'If you could just answer the question?'

Paxman wasn't the only person to shout at me over the years. Lots of people did. They shouted various things.

'Who let *you* in?' I got that off Cilla Black once, as she swung round to find me breaking into her TV studio.

'I'm going to break your legs!' That was from a fuming pop star.

1

And, 'What do you think you're doing?' I got that one quite a lot over the years. Simon Cowell used it when he found me rifling through his bedroom drawers one afternoon. A date once incorporated it into a 'you're dumped' speech, after I explained I was unavoidably delayed due to being stuck at a swinging party in Cardiff. In time, I would start to say it to myself in the mirror most mornings.

I was warned though. I can never say I wasn't warned. On my first ever day on work experience for a newspaper, I had been taken aside by a woman in a sharply creased shirt with a face that matched. She did her best to convince me to make it my last day.

'You realise you'll never marry if you become a tabloid journalist,' she had sighed over a Marlboro and a pre-noon vodka. 'The only men that will ever understand the mad things we do all day are other male journalists. And trust me, you don't *ever* want to date one of them.'

In retrospect, this was my first 'what do you think you're doing?' speech. A warning. A premonition of the consequences of the ruthless tabloid world. This battle-weary, embittered woman, who was hurtling towards forty under a single duvet; beaten down, looking back and regretting her life. Bravely trying to warn the next generation against making the same, terrible mistake.

Naturally, I completely ignored her.

Which was a shame. Because one decade, several unrequited love affairs and many hours spent getting shouted at by prostitutes, pop stars and maniacal transsexuals later, I began to think that maybe she was right.

*

2

So what was I doing back then? Well, I was desperately, *desperately*, trying to get into tabloid journalism and had just arrived in London, convinced I only had to step off the train and I'd walk straight into a job.

I didn't. Tabloid newspapers are notoriously difficult to get into for complete beginners, unless you happen to be related to, or sleeping with, someone important who's already employed on one. I wasn't. So I had been reduced to months of unsuccessful begging by letter, phone and email instead.

Looking back I'm not surprised I was unsuccessful. I had no job history. No scoops. No experience. I had just one celebrity name in my contacts book – Roland Rat, who I'd interviewed for my college magazine. I may have written in my letters that I would make a fantastic tabloid journalist and they'd be mad to turn me down, but rat interviews, even celebrity ones, do not impress Fleet Street. No one took my calls. They all turned me down.

Six months later I was still in London and living in a hostel. I had enough left on my overdraft for one more week of trying, before I'd have to admit defeat and take the train back home to my parents in Lancashire.

Finally, in an act of complete desperation, I tried bribery. De Beers. Well, De Lagers anyway. I took ten crates of Fosters to a national newspaper and stood next to them, waiting, CV in hand, until the News Editor arrived at work. I blocked his route to the lifts, said I was the mad woman who rang every morning and that I would do anything, *anything*, to get a job on a tabloid newspaper. And I had brought beer.

My Fleet Street career started the next morning.

*

Actually, when I say 'career' I may be exaggerating slightly. I was only actually given one twelve-hour shift, but that is as good as it gets when you're starting in tabloid journalism.

You never walk straight into a staff job in newspapers. Well, unless you've got someone on the management floor you regularly get to see in their pyjamas and call 'darling'. For everyone else the best way in is to fight your way up through the nightmare known as the casual shift system. This is basically a legalised form of slave labour, and where I started.

A casual shift basically means you've been hired for a one-day trial. During this day you must do everything that is asked of you, no matter how ridiculous, impossible, improbable, illegal or immoral it sounds. At the end of the day you will either get fired and they will never take your calls again, or, if you're really lucky, you get to come back and start the whole process again in the morning. Repeat this process for weeks, months, even years. If you survive you may, one day, finally, be given a staff job.

As a casual shifter you have no rights, no commitment, and have absolutely no idea what Hell will be unleashed on you that day.

I didn't realise quite what I had just got myself into. I didn't know that I was actually begging to start a life where I'd routinely be asked to do three impossible things before breakfast and be sworn at by four celebrities by lunch. A life where 'alien seduction catsuit' would soon be seen as an entirely reasonable thing to write down on an expenses claim. As would 'accidental donkey burial', 'lamb shank bait for mythical beast' and '£500 cash in brown envelope as requested by TV star'.

4

FOREWORD

I certainly didn't know that within hours of starting my tabloid life, I'd be coming face-to-face with my all-time small-screen idol, and go through the agony of being forced to knock him back flat.

I just thought, Hey, I've finally got a job in tabloids.

1

MY MATT LEBLANC HEARTACHE

And the Art of Annoying A-listers

On my first day at work I rode up the tube escalator past adverts featuring happy people who were thinner than me and I thought, I'd better make this work. After all, sod all else was going right in my life.

I was single. Although there were six billion people in the world, so far none of them had said they wanted me as their girlfriend. I tried not to dwell on it though.

And I was still living in that hostel. I slept on the bottom half of a single bunk-bed. My four-foot-wide home was shared with a trainee ballerina who would awake each morn at 5 am and click each of her joints individually, whilst performing warm-up exercises holding on to the sink that jutted out behind my pillow. By the time she moved on to leg extensions at 5.15 am, the cramped space ensured her bunions inevitably ended up under my nose. That and the constant cracking would signal it was time to get up.

I complained at the time, but to her credit she is one of the few living things that has ever proved willing to share my bedroom on a regular basis. We've lost touch so I never got chance to thank her, but I still sometimes go to the ballet and see if I can hear her.

Back then I was just desperate to get out of that hostel and into a higher thread-count of bed sheet. Or, at the very least, perhaps upgrade to a top-bunk option that would prove bunion proof.

I was skint. It had been twenty-four long weeks since I had left my old childhood bed and taken the train from Lancashire down to London. My parents had waved me off at Preston station, asking, 'Was I sure?'. I'd dismissed all concerns with a merry wave of my Roland Rat exclusive and reassured them I'd be fine. How hard could it be?

Rejection does not pay well. At the time of the beer stunt I was facing eviction from the dorm unless I paid the rent within seven days. My sole possessions – stored on the shelf behind my pillow – were a half-smoked box of Silk Cut Ultra Low cigarettes and a tray of Pot Noodles.

In retrospect, the battle-weary News Editor had probably hired me as a joke. I'm sure he just wished this annoying girl in reception would piss off and leave him alone with the beer. But I was like a persistent mosquito and begged and begged. Plus, I made sure I was sitting on the crates when I spoke to him, so there was no way he could get at them until he said yes. In the end, he gave in. He said yes. Yes. I could come in the next day.

For me, this first day was the start of a new life. I rang home and gave the good news. I was finally in. Nothing, but nothing, was going to stop me having a career in newspapers.

It's lucky I had such a positive attitude really, because I arrived for my first day in tabloid newspapers to find a man brandishing a Kalashnikov at the newsdesk.

The gunman appeared to be screaming. I couldn't make out exactly what he was saying, as the thick glass entrance doors to the office were guarded with a swipe lock system. The temporary paper pass I'd just been issued with at reception didn't seem to open it. To be honest, I'd been so busy flailing ineffectually at the swipe system and wondering if it was a sacking offence to be unable to open a door, that I'd completely failed to notice the unfolding drama on the other side of the glass.

I stared through the glass at the scene inside. The newsroom appeared to be under siege. Although there was what seemed to be a life-sized Dalek in the way, blocking some of the view, from what I could see the man with the gun looked quite angry. And appeared to be shouting at the beer-taking News Editor I'd met the day before.

Had a terrorist broken in? Had I just blundered into a massive story on my first day? Would I have to save the day and the entire office's staff? I prepared to dial 999. My college media course had tended to major on shorthand, not firearms. Still, I flattened myself to the wall like I'd seen the coppers do in *The Bill*, and I peered through the glass door again.

There were about sixty people inside, but none of them appeared to be paying all that much attention to the ranting gunman. Which seemed a bit odd. They were on the phone. Looking bored, even. One was sitting flicking through *Hello!*. Maybe this sort of thing happened all the time . . .

'Trying to get in?' yawned an Essex-twanged voice behind me. It was a man in his late thirties, who smelt of fresh whisky despite it not yet being 9 am. He wore a suit that had once been handsome and well-structured but was now distinctly battle-weary. His face matched.

'Yeah. Umm, there's a man with a gun in there though,' I pointed out. Quite casually given the circumstances, I thought. I was trying to look like I dealt with gunmen all the time back home. The creased man looked in, and sighed. He fished out his plastic security pass, and brandished it at the door which clicked open.

'That's just one of the reporters. Nothing to worry about.'

As the door swung open, I could hear the gunman screaming, 'I risked my fucking life. My fucking life and *that's* on the front.'

Creased Man waved me in and nodded at the gunman. 'He's spent three months single-handedly infiltrating an international arms dealers' network, and just discovered they're going to splash on my pics of Madonna in her knickers instead. Happy days.'

'Why?' the gunman was wailing hysterically inside. '*Why*? I could have died and the Department of Silly Stories gets the front page for *that*?'

Creased Man shrugged in the gunman's direction and walked nonchalantly through the line of fire.

'It's *Madge*,' he tutted as he passed. 'In her *pants*. Where else does he think they're going to put it?'

I ducked and followed. Creased Man stuck out his hand to me on the way. 'Mark Crump, staff reporter,' he said. 'Department of Silly Stories,' he added, raising his voice in the gunman's direction.

I had only enough time to congratulate Crump on his success with Madonna's knickers and tell him it was my first day before the man with the gun let out another howl, hurled the AK-47 to the floor and stormed out the door behind us.

The office fell silent. Heads turned expectantly towards a blacked-out glass office to the right.

'Tosser!' a male voice rasped out from behind the glass.

'And that,' muttered Crump, nodding his head in the direction of the office as he scuttled past, 'is The Editor.'

Crump neatly stepped over the AK-47, giving it just the merest of curious glances on the way, and turned to wink at me, 'Welcome on board.'

I stood, staring, as he reached for a form marked 'Expenses' from a fifty-something motherly type, sitting behind a large desk laden with small glass phials. I recognised her as Anne, the newsdesk secretary, who had helped load the lager into the News Editor's car the previous day.

'What's that?' asked Crump, holding up one of the phials to the light.

'GHB,' Anne answered. 'Investigations brought it in yesterday. Liquid Ecstasy. Gamma-hydroxybutrate to give it its full kennel name.'

Crump opened the phial and swigged. 'So it is,' he nodded. And headed to his desk.

I thought it best not to mention any of this when I phoned home later that day.

'Well? How's it going?' Mum had asked.

'Oh, fine,' I replied. 'Everyone seems really nice . . .'

I was soon to understand why a sedative drug is a perfectly reasonable breakfast to set you up for a day in tabloid journalism. For my first ever assignment, on my first ever day, I found myself starring in an iconic scene of *Friends*, praying that the actress in a wedding dress, who was standing right in front of me, would not recognise me as the pesky hack who'd been hammering on her front door just hours earlier.

To explain what on earth I was doing there, praying in front of TV brides in the first place, let me explain the tabloid reporter evolutionary system, and my lowly place in it at this given time.

'And who,' said the News Editor wearily, as I approached his desk with my best happy-to-help smile on my first day, 'are you?'

Not the warmest of welcomes, but not entirely his fault. A News Editor is in charge of sourcing, coordinating and overseeing every news story in the paper and checking no one will get sued, sacked or killed if it gets printed. A News Editor may be coordinating up to fifty people, on several continents. Today, on top of that, he had a Kalashnikov-wielding reporter and a very angry Editor to deal with.

So, not the easiest of jobs. And it was not surprising that the exhausted-looking hack with the bloodshot eyes and ink-stained tie couldn't quite remember the girl from Lancashire with the unremarkable CV who he'd fleetingly met in reception the previous day. I reminded him about the beer and he remembered. News Editors always remember free beer.

'Oh, it's you,' he said, with a nod. 'You're shifting aren't you? Go on, go and sit with the others. Over there.'

The Others turned out to be a row of six other grimly determined shifters. They, like me, were all in new suits. They too had all been hired that day. And they too had all arrived at the office that morning thinking they'd just started a career in tabloid newspapers. They smiled at me with hatred as I approached the row of chairs and sat down. So. There was yet another shifter. Yet another rival. Yet another person who was desperate to get the job.

A newspaper will hire several shift workers at once and will tell them all that they are in with a chance of that golden prize of the staff job.

To give you an idea of the odds: hundreds of these shift workers are hired each year, but perhaps just one or two make it through and eventually get a staff position. Staff jobs do not emerge that often, you see. You have to wait until the previous occupant either gets promoted, poached, fired, rehabbed, carried out in a wooden box or, and this only happens very occasionally, makes it through to a happy retirement.

Meanwhile the sea of shifters grows and we all fight for that one job. To be the one that's chosen you must be prepared to beg, to plot, to scheme, to suck up furiously to all the right people and most of all, to deliver. How are you going to get that killer story that will make your name? How are you going to get noticed? How are you going to stitch up your rivals and make sure you win the staff job prize? These are the challenges that face a trainee tabloid hack.

The process is all a bit like *The Apprentice*, except that you don't get to stay in a penthouse flat because the wages are dreadful. But you do turn up each day wondering what they're going to make you do next, and if you're going to get fired.

One of the line of six shifters I clocked as I sat down had a desk full of the glass phials and was already storming away on his keyboard. 'Exclusive' he was typing with a flourish, as we other shifters glared at him in envy. I picked up a discarded *Hello!*, flicked through my blank notepad and tried to look equally busy and important. Damn. I hadn't thought to bring any drugs investigations with me. I suddenly realised getting into the building was the easy bit. My fight to get employed on a tabloid newspaper was far from over.

'Come here!' the News Editor yelled, with a gesture to one of The Others, and a shifter was summoned over to the news desk. He left thirty seconds later with instructions to knock on Ulrika Jonsson's door and ask her something impertinent about a footballer. He was armed with a notepad and a hopeful expression.

'Doomed!' I heard a whisper from behind the Dalek. It was Crump. And he didn't appear to have full control of his eyeballs. 'Ulrika never talks. Well, not to the likes of us red-top scumbags.' He swatted an imaginary fly off his nose.

His eyeballs may have been uncoordinated, but Crump's thoughts were not. 'Red tops' is the nickname given to the tabloid titles which splash their names in a bright red box so they look nice and friendly to the punters on the stands. 'Buy me!' the red box screams. 'Buy me! Because I'm fun and I'm packed with amazing stories of celebrity and sex and scandal and good things like that.' But whilst a red top may look friendly on a newsagent's shelf, they're not always welcomed with open arms by the people who appear in them.

The red-top shifter on his way to Ulrika's would be met with a firmly closed door. 'He'll be sat there 'til Friday when the *OK!* staffer turns up with a cheque and it's Game Over,' muttered Crump. 'Poor sod. None of the staffers are touching that one with a bargepole.'

There is an evolutionary scale in newspapers. We shifters, I soon realised, were right at the bottom of it. Pond life. The lowest life form. A brainless, faceless, scum-sucking primordial sludge who get sent to do all the impossible jobs in newspapers that no sane person would ever agree to. Like going round knocking on celebrities' front doors and asking them idiot questions, which everyone back in the office knows you really haven't a hope in hell of getting answered.

But there is hope and there is an evolutionary path. From here, with luck and time and a few scoops in the paper, you will perhaps develop into a staff reporter like Crump. This is a much better position to be in. You get an expense account to cover your bar bills for a start, and the authority to start ordering shifters to do all really impossible jobs you don't want to do yourself because you know they haven't a hope in hell of working.

And from there it goes up, up through the ranks of News

Editors, Associate Editors, Assistant Editors and Deputy Editors. Until, if you stay alive long enough, you can climb right to the top of the tabloid tree and become The Editor. The Editor is the one who gets to think up all the impossible jobs in the first place. And then shout at people when it doesn't work.

So, tabloid-wise I was right at the bottom of the ladder. Festering at the back of the newsroom and awaiting my fate. From my seat amongst the sludge of shifters, I stared at the room whence the shout of 'tosser' had emerged. The Editor's office. I stared and wondered what sort of beast lived within.

The Editor's office was a bunker-like affair with blacked out windows; it took up around half the length of the whole office. Outside hung a series of six-foot-high framed images of previous front pages – or splashes – from the paper. Tales of shamed TV hosts in sex dungeons, or film stars on drugs, headlines about cheating sportsmen, giant images of sobbing betrayed women and of randy royals caught misbehaving. These posters were all there, I presumed, as a general, six-foot-high reminder of the sort of thing The Editor was after. I stared, panicking. I hadn't brought any dungeon investigations in with me either.

'Nine o'clock Conference, ladies and gentlemen, please,' announced Anne, politely. She had a cut-glass English accent which was perfect for fending off furious lawyers first thing in the mornings.

There was a murmuring as people began to gather papers and a stream of suited men and a couple of women approached the blacked out glass, looking worried. Crump was the only one smiling. He also appeared to be tap-dancing.

'We're off to see The Editor, the wonderful Editor of us,' he snorted as he passed, clutching a picture of Jennifer Ellison in a bikini. 'Got splash written all over it,' he shimmied as he passed.

Each day, early in the morning, a newspaper Conference is held in the bunker. The Editor gathers his top reporters, the heads of departments, and his top lawyers and there's a thirty minute debate over what should go in the next issue.

Should you ever find yourself having to take part in one, the trick to remember is this: basically – in The Editor's mind at least – these meetings are based on a system quite similar to the one the Pope operates. The Editor is always right. No matter what he says, everyone will always agree that it's the right decision. Paper infallibility. He, and it is usually a he on the tabloids, tells his minions what he wants in the paper and everyone else in the room agrees and then works out how they are going to do it.

On this particular morning the cast of the US sitcom *Friends* had just descended on London to film a wedding between Ross (David Schwimmer) and his English fiancée Emily (*Cold Feet* star Helen Baxendale). Surely, said The Editor, surely if someone just popped round to Helen Baxendale's house that morning, she'd tell us all about the top-secret *Friends* plot, and then invite us in to give us a nice free exclusive about her recently announced pregnancy to boot.

Naturally, the News Editor would have assured The Editor that this was a great idea, it was all in hand and they were all right on it. The Showbiz Editor would have provided home addresses and filming schedules and the staff reporters would have made absolutely sure that they were not the ones to be sent on this impossible task, by suggesting other, urgent things they had to do. All they needed now, the News Editor presumably thought as he exited Conference, was a freelance sucker on the shifting desk who was willing to go on this doomed job.

Seconds later I was stepping over the AK-47, past a giant front page containing an extremely unfortunate revelation about Frank Bough, and leaving the office for my first ever impossible celebrity doorstep.

A 'doorstep' is the term for a journalist arriving, uninvited and unannounced, at someone's, usually a celebrity's, house, knocking on the door and then asking a highly impertinent question.

It's called a doorstep because you literally hang about, standing on their doorstep until you get an answer to your question. On big stories there could be up to twenty reporters outside, jostling for position on said doorstep.

As far as I have been able to understand, in The Editor's head the scenario is supposed to go something like this:

Journalist: Knock Knock.
Celebrity opens door with a broad, welcoming smile:
Why, hello there. Good morning. And who are you?
Journalist: Hello. I'm from a tabloid newspaper. Now then, could you tell me about your latest film project/sex scandal/embarrassing disease/event that has just rocked your world?
Celebrity: Yes of course. I'd love to. Please come in. Tea or coffee? And I presume you'd like some pictures?

In the entire history of doorsteps, not one has ever followed this script.

Once a woman was convinced I was her long-lost daughter and fell into my arms sobbing. Sometimes there's anger. Like that pop star who threatened to break my legs. A touch dramatic that one. 'No comment' does the job perfectly sufficiently. Sometimes there's a request for cash – one particular soap star used to demand you drove to the bank, came back with the agreed amount of loot in your boot and would then send his wife to bank it in their account. You'd have to wait on the doorstep until she rang to confirm it had been passed over the bank counter, whereupon we'd then be invited in for the chat on the strict understanding that the quotes would be attributed to 'a close friend' and a sentence would be added at the end claiming he had 'refused to comment'. His bosses would ring the paper on the morning the story appeared, laughing at the last bit and asking how much he'd got.

Sometimes the reaction was one of understandable bewilderment. Like the day a newspaper boss had a dream that a top TV personality had died and ordered the reporters to knock on her door 'to see if the dream was true'. The startled star was greeted with a lilied floral arrangement and a reporter earnestly asking, 'would you say that you were ill at all?' Could have been worse. There had been a lengthy office debate about whether he should take a floral wreath spelling out her name.

I have always rather admired actress Helen Baxendale's method of dispatching me and my persistent request on this particular day. No doubt sick to death of a stream of reporters knocking on her door (we were, we later found out, the fourth that morning) she simply opened her front door and her two very large and extremely friendly pet dogs cheerfully chased me all the way down tc the garden gate.

I arrived, panting, at Stoke Newington High Street, where I had to phone the desk and admit that I had nothing to file other than a woof, and a 'Heel! Down! No! Oh, sorry! Come here!' from Miss Baxendale, who I remember had attempted to bring her large, playful, and incredibly enthusiastic pets to heel as they joyfully toyed with their latest visitor. I hadn't stuck around long enough to actually ask any questions of their owner. Nothing on the pregnancy. Nothing on *Friends*. I was only two hours into my Fleet Street career and I had failed already.

There was a silence at the end of the phone. 'Heel?', asked the News Editor. '*That's* your interview? Heel?'

I said I'd learn. I reminded him about the beer.

'Okay,' he said. 'The Editor's just had a great idea. He wants you to break into the *Friends* set instead.'

Should you ever find yourself in a similar situation – tasked with breaking into a top-security film set filled with Holly-wood A-listers, their personal security guards and several members of the Met police force – here's how to do it. Buy fifty Big Macs. With added chips.

It worked this time anyway. I reached the cordon guarded by the burly security guys, gave them my biggest smile and said I was 'helping catering' (which was true. I had brought food so I was, technically, helping them). 'Are you crew?' I asked. 'Would you like a burger?' The way to the heart of most heavily guarded activities, I later came to realise, is via

Security's stomachs. They took the burgers with a smile, helped themselves to chips, gave me a wristband and waved me past. I was in.

Somehow, maybe it was the wristband, maybe it was the fact that I'd supersized and gone for added cheese, but everyone I met proved willing to swallow not only the contents of my tray, but also the improbable line that I was an 'extra'. I watched from just feet away as Richard Branson came to film his cameo role as a novelty hat salesman (that Branson chap can run a business and his airline's service is second-to-none, but God he's a *lousy* actor – he took take after take and eventually his few lines were cut down and Matt LeBlanc ended up improvising over them instead), Matthew Perry popped over from Westminster Abbey where he'd been filming with the Duchess of York (a one-take wonder, apparently) and was excitedly showing off his home-movie footage of Fergie waving and saying 'Hello Chandler!' down the lens. Scripts were left on tables. Plots were spilled. And every half hour I'd run to the loo and, screened by constant flushing, I'd file, file, file, every cough and spit of every conversation on my mobile to the waiting newsdesk.

Twenty gallons of flush later, I was thinking this was all going very well. I was feeling rather smug, actually. Especially when I noticed all the other journalists being turned away by Security. I was inches away from my all-time favourite TV people on my all-time favourite show and, when not encased in the loo with my nose pressed to the cistern, I was having an absolute whale of a time.

Then it all went wrong. 'OK, extras,' said the director,

gesturing in my suddenly panic-stricken direction. 'We need you all for this next little scene.' I was ushered into make-up.

If you ever see the *Friends* episode called 'The One With Ross's Wedding', you can witness for yourself what happened next. Look closely and you can just about make me out. I'm behind Chandler and Ross, opposite Rachel, the one in the white suit about half way down the pews. The one who appears to be in a heavily agitated sweat, hunched, shaking and with a neck craned at an awkward angle to hide her face as the bride sweeps past. The 'little scene' turned out to be the one where the radiant bride – played by the aforementioned dog-owning Helen Baxendale – appears in church. She was minus her dogs, fortunately, but I still wasn't happy to see her. I had to sit in that pew for three solid, terrifying hours, almost wetting myself in fear each time the bride swept by. Every time I heard her taffeta make its rustling approach, my stomach would turn to water at the thought that she might spot and identify me as the complete idiot who'd come knocking on her front door a few hours earlier.

Worse still, the newsdesk was phoning me every half hour requesting updates and demanding I file. My mobile phone was set to vibrate, and obscenities began buzzing into my kidneys every ten minutes, with the desk growing increasingly irate as the evening deadline for the paper drew near. In the end I had to fake a series of violent stomach upsets so I could run to the loos to hunch over the cistern and phone in the in-demand copy.

It was a lie I came to regret when it came to Matt LeBlanc. Oh Matt LeBlanc. The tousle-haired Love God with the get-into-that-bed-right-now eyes. My idol. My favourite. And I met him. I met him and he was more gorgeous than I ever imagined. And, he spoke to me.

I had long rehearsed in my head, and indeed my bed, what I would say if I ever met Matt LeBlanc. How much I loved his Joey Tribbiani. How good he'd been in the little-seen *Top of the Heap*, perhaps. I was even prepared to discuss the finer points of his fleeting appearance in a Jon Bon Jovi music video in 1990.

And I had my chance. With filming over, he was in the process of breaking open a bottle in his dressing room and inviting everyone to join him. As an extra, as an acting colleague, as, indeed, a *Friend*, I was being waved into the inner sanctum. Into a slice of Matt LeBlanc heaven. But, with my pager vibrating angrily to demands from the newsdesk that I filed 'right fucking now!', I had to make my excuses and leave.

And thus, all I said to my TV hero, my TV hero who was sitting in front of me looking totally, undeniably shaggable and inviting me to drink vodka in his dressing room, all I said to this God of the small screen, was, 'Sorry, got to go mate. I've got the trots.'

By the time I'd finished filing, I emerged from the loo to find the cast had left in their limos. Joey Tribbiani had left the building. With Chandler. With Monica. With Rachel. Without me.

The story never ran. 'Bloody American sitcom rubbish,' said The Editor the next day, and ran the Jennifer Ellison pic instead. Of course, everyone agreed. The Editor is always right.

I read my *Friends*-free paper alone on my bunk-bed, and wept.

'How come it's not in the paper?' my mother asked, the next morning.

I'd rung the previous night in between toilet breaks, recounting tales of hanging out with the cast of *Friends*. It all sounded great, they said. Brilliant fun. Success at last, hey? A girl from Lancashire hanging out with the Hollywood A-listers. Just wait 'til all my old college mates read about this. After six months of having to report I was 'penniless and living in a hostel', this was all much better news.

I explained about The Editor changing his mind.

'Never mind,' said mum. 'Better luck next time. They'll have something else exciting for you in the office today. Don't forget to ring and tell us all about it.'

This was to be the last time in about a decade that I had an honest conversation with my parents about what had been said or done in the office that day. Turned out that the gunman and drugs had merely been a warm up. Yes there was 'something exciting' in store for me, but it proved to be something that I definitely couldn't tell my parents about.

2

MY WIFE-
SWAPPING SHAME

*And the Art of Attending
Swinging Parties*

As a reward for my undercover cistern work, I was not fired. I was given another twenty-four hours of employment. The News Editor even remembered who I was when I got to the office. In the casual shift system, this was practically a relationship.

I was ignored by the other shifters though. They glared at me with jealousy as I approached. Word of me hanging out with Matt LeBlanc and being greeted by the News Editor soon spread. We were at war. The really good news though, was that there was one less of us. A chair was empty – one of The Others had been fired the previous day.

There are press offices for the emergency services that

reporters can call for information on major stories. If there is a traffic accident, you can ring the press office who will give you details of the incident and the casualties, which you can use to file a report. However, the previous day, a car accident had happened just a couple of miles down the road from the newspaper headquarters. The police and ambulance services had no details when they were called, so a shifter had been told to hop into his car, pop down there to see what had happened and 'see what you can pick up'.

They'd hoped for a few quotes. Perhaps a chat with any onlookers? Maybe a quote from the victims or police workers at the scene . . .

That's not quite what happened though.

Three hours later the reporter returned, carrying a hub cab and part of a tyre. He'd emptied it from a bin-liner onto the News Editor's desk to a stunned silence. The News Editor had stared for a while, trying to remember what story the man had gone on.

'You said to see what I could pick up . . .?' the shifter had started nervously. 'This is all I could get. The police had cordoned the motorway off. It was really difficult to run past the barriers and across the lanes to get it.'

'What the . . .?' the News Editor had spluttered, as a crowd gathered.

'He's brought the fucking car in,' yelled The Editor, coming out of his office to look, as the shifter froze into silence, realising he'd just done something Very Wrong.

The bin-bag was given back to the shifter and he was asked to clear his desk into it. The News Editor was still laughing about it the next morning as I came into the office.

'See what you can pick up! Can you bloody believe it?' he was shouting down the phone as I approached his desk.

It turned out he was talking to a foreign reporter in a war zone, on an emergency line, at vast international expense. 'Thought you'd like to know,' said the News Editor. 'Tell the lads. What a toss pot! Daren't send him to cover a funeral. He'd come back with the bloody coffin! Anyway, how's the war? Shall I send him over?'

Finally, after debating whether a cruise missile would fit in a bin-bag, the News Editor came off the phone and looked up.

'Oh, hi,' he said. 'Okay, The Editor is very pleased with your breaking and entering work. Tip top, well done. And he's come up with an absolutely brilliant idea for your next shift. He says he wants you to go wife swapping.'

'Oh, fabulous,' I had replied.

You can see why I didn't mention it to my parents.

I hadn't been wife swapping before. I was never one to get invited to those sort of parties. Presumably because I've never had any sort of husband to swap. Reporting on them had never been covered in my journalism course either. In fact, looking back, the only thing of relevance I ever learned during that course was the shorthand bit. I could write 'kinky housewife' in 0.5 seconds. But had no idea how to go about finding one, and getting her into a paper.

But tabloid journalism is a craft you learn on the job. And I was taught all I needed to learn about the subject during a four-hour drive from London to Blackpool by a man from the Investigations department called Mike (not the AK-47 owner, he was still AWOL on his Madonna-related strop).

Now Mike had a world-weary air about him. He'd been to two vice dens that week already, and it was only Wednesday. Frankly he said, as he set off with me to his third, he was a bit bored of the whole thing.

The story was that a woman, a pillar of the community type, was running a vice den in her suburban home. Total strangers were rampaging through her house once a week for £60 a head, and allegedly doing unspeakable things to each other within full earshot of her semi-detached neighbours. The neighbours in question had rung the newsdesk to demand an exposé, in the hope they'd shame her into moving. They had understandable worries about the effect on house prices.

We were to attend, witness the debauchery, film what we could reasonably show in a family newspaper, get enough to write a thundering piece about the morality of Britain being in decline, make our excuses, and leave.

'Try and think how to work in a pun about the Blackpool Tower,' added the News Editor as I left.

I nodded eagerly, trying to make it look as if I went to vice dens all the time and couldn't wait for my next one.

Should you ever find yourself having to go undercover at a wife-swapping party, this is how it is done.

'We say we're a married couple but we're having problems,' instructed Mike as we pulled onto the M1. 'The best thing to do is to tell everybody that it's your first time so you're "nervous" and therefore you "just want to watch". Everyone will understand this. These things are actually all really polite and no one will hassle you to take part. That would be seen as rude ... Yes, *I know* a massive partner-swap session *is* rude,' he responded to my startled eyebrows at this point, 'but, funnily enough, they're never usually conducted with anything other than impeccable manners,' he added. 'The best thing to do is actually say very little. Don't start conversations or fire off lots of questions – that will be seen as suspicious. And the less information you give, the less you'll have to remember later.

'I'll have a camera hidden in my jacket zip which will record everything. So don't stand directly in front of me or you'll block my filming, just stand to one side, watch, observe, and let me do the talking. If I'm chatting to someone, shut up, so only their voice will appear on the tape. Never talk over them 'cos we'll need the tape as evidence. And don't get drunk. Oh, and don't join in. One of our reporters once went to cover a kinky husband and wife who ran a B&B, but ended up being recorded on their CCTV system doing something most untoward at the foot of their bed. The footage was on the internet for months afterwards. It's still on the Picture Editor's screensaver.'

I nodded as if I went to wife-swap parties all the time, and so obviously I knew the rules by now.

'Of course,' Mike warned as we hit the M6, 'we're going to have to get our cover stories straight. One false bit of information and we'll be caught out. No matter how wildly sexually uninhibited and exciting people are, they rarely want the entire nation reading all about their sex lives over a bowl of cornflakes.'

So, all the way up to Blackpool we practised being a 'couple'. Actually I'd been single for about a year at this time so was quite excited at the idea of being able to tell people I had a boyfriend. Even if I'd only borrowed him for the after-noon to go wife swapping.

What was our job? (We decided to say teachers – 'undercover-journalists' being an answer that would go down quite badly, according to Mike.) Where had we met? How old were we? Our star signs? Any brothers or sisters? Pets? Did the other person smoke? What did they drink? Where did we live? Were we married? (I was actually getting quite caught up in the whole charade and wanted to go for 'yes' at this point, but Mike downgraded us to a long-term couple, saying it would stop any awkward questions about proposals, wed-ding ceremonies and as my fingers were clearly ringless, would also mean avoiding extra jewellery expenses.) Any tattoos? Interesting bodily defects? What was our favourite sexual position?

Mike said this was the way the script tended to go at every swinging party he went to and I had no reason to doubt his superior wisdom.

We tested each other thoroughly and by the time we smelt the sea, I was rehearsed, ready, and raring to go. Although slightly disappointed that I couldn't even get my fake boyfriend to make a commitment.

I had worn a black polo neck, black trousers and flat shoes for the occasion of my first day's wife swapping. Mike had looked at me and shaken his head.

'You might want to look like you're a little more up for it,' he said. In the end we stopped at a seaside boutique and I compromised on a camisole top and wished I'd shaved under my arms.

Mike had stopped, briefly, at a motorway service station,

half an hour before starting the job. He had, and there's no delicate way of putting this, gone in to the smallest room with a lad's mag, *Razzle* I think. He asked for a receipt and said he fully intended to claim it on expenses.

'Sorry about that,' he said, as he returned to the car five minutes later. 'Just had to disarm.'

Apparently – and I was learning a lot that afternoon that had not been on my media studies course – it's really difficult for a man to make his excuses and leave a wife-swapping party if he's visibly, shall we say, *enjoying* the proceedings. Many an investigation has gone wrong when a male journalist attempts to tell a prostitute that he isn't interested, but his towel tells an entirely different tale. A 'disarming' chat is given to every rookie male hack on undercover vice jobs when they first start in tabloid journalism. It's a wisdom that's handed down through the generations. It stops any such 'misunderstandings', and makes it much easier all round if any camera footage has to be produced in court as part of an investigation. Or used as a screensaver.

Mike's attention to detail and pre-job preparation was commendable, but I'm not sure he needed quite so many precautions in the end. For we arrived at the party to find the hostess was not quite the body beautiful. We'd had to email over photos of ourselves the night before to win admission to the party, and it had been quickly and enthusiastically given. Once we got there we could see why.

The hostess greeted us in a red nylon negligee and all-over dimples. I remember thinking that I needn't have worried so much about my own personal grooming; she really could have taken a little more care herself if she was going to go that short in the skirt department.

She opened the door an inch, asked our names and for the confirmation code Mike had been given. Then she relieved us both of our £60 entrance fee in the hallway, which was painted in magnolia and held a rather fetching picture of a woodland scene.

We then entered an extremely bizarre party.

In the pristine kitchen it was all cheese straws and polite conversation over the dishwasher. There was a No Smoking policy too, I was told as the hostess banished my pack of twenty Silk Cut with an abrupt, 'Outside in the garden please!' Great. So it was fine to come in and have nookie with total strangers, but could I please keep my appalling nicotine habit well out of sight?

Only the hostess was in a state of undress. Everyone else was dressed normally – smart casual I'd say – and having normal conversations, shaking hands, introducing themselves and complimenting the hostess on her decor (both the soft furnishings and her outfit). We sipped wine and picked at canapés, which were, we had been assured on the phone, 'all fully provided with the entrance fee'.

Most attendees were in their late forties or early fifties. Smartly dressed, well spoken, holding hands with their spouses. Mike grabbed a couple of vol-au-vents and started chatting to a couple standing nearby. There was a retired copper and his charming wife. To our left was an estate agent.

A morose man sidled up to me. 'I'm an accountant,' he said. 'There. I've bored you already.' And he sidled off again. Rather excitingly, another man claimed to be in MI5, and another said he was a helicopter pilot. I was just thinking it was actually a very good place to meet people, before I realised that like us 'teachers', they were both probably lying through their teeth. Talk was of children, jobs, mortgages. It was like being at a dinner party with your parents. A child's drawings were Sellotaped on the wall. The hostess's son, she said. He was with his grandparents. Doing well at school.

After an hour we moved on to pensions. To be honest, by this stage I felt a bit let down at my first vice den, and was feeling sick from all the cheese straws.

Then the bloke next to me took all his clothes off.

I watched, speechless, as he unveiled his paunch, and stood, proudly leaning against the kitchen counter and smiling in my direction. He hadn't disarmed, I noticed. I realised with horror that he wasn't the only one undressing. It was like a silent klaxon had gone off. Everyone was getting naked. In a slow, orderly pace. They all folded their clothes, I noticed.

I felt the hostess stroking my arm. 'We're going to go upstairs and play now,' she said. 'Join us.'

Blind panic.

I looked wildly around at Mike, who was deep in conversation with the man who claimed to work for MI5. I could see Mike was pointing his jacket at him, filming, whilst he figured out if the man was worth a 'Double Oh Oh!' type story.

I had my own 'Oh Oh' drama going on though. 'Mike?' I squeaked. He turned round, saw the white acres of flesh being exposed around him and the whites of my eyes as I watched. He sauntered over. 'She just wants to watch, don't you sweetie?' he said patting my bum. 'She's a bit frigid since she put on all the weight.'

I gave him my best Paddington Bear stare.

But the line was, undeniably, effective. Most occupants gave a sigh of understanding and an encouraging smile in my direction as they continued to disrobe. They then filed out of the room one by one, giving me encouraging pats on the arm as they left and saying they 'understood'.

It was all incredibly polite, as if they'd just been called to a banquet by the Master of Ceremonies at a formal ball.

Up the stairs they went. Up past the bathroom with the avocado toilet suite with peach bath towels hung neatly on the railings. Upwards past the room on the left marked 'No Entry!', where a Superman duvet and a sprinkling of kid's toys marked it out as the son's bedroom. I sincerely hoped he was staying at the grandparents' overnight. Or his 'what I did at the weekend' essay might prove a bit startling for his teachers.

On they all went to the furthest room at the end of the corridor, where there were flatteringly low lighting levels, and a black satin sheet had been flung over a double divan bed, as an erotic contrast to its rather chintzy peach velvet headrest.

'Come on, then,' urged Mike, and I braced myself and followed. I poked my head round the door. It was not pretty in there. All was total silence but for the noise of sagging flesh grimly slapping against peach velvet. And the hostess, in her lace-edged camisole leaning over at one point to cajole again, 'join us'.

I went back to the cheese straws.

I left Mike in position at the door, pointing his jacket at the proceedings and was sitting in the kitchen when the first of the women filed down a few minutes later. Clothes back on,

34

they had reverted back to middle-class manners and matronly concern.

'It's okay,' said one, as she brought over a bottle of wine. 'I hated it at first as well. But you get used to it.'

There were three of them who all said the same. All in their late forties. All married. And all of them having left their husbands upstairs, on the satin-clad bed with the nylon-clad hostess.

It's much easier interviewing people when they've got their clothes on, I found. I asked one wife what she was doing here. 'My husband had an affair, and this is the compromise we've reached to stay together,' she said. 'Twice a year we come to a party like this, he does what he has to do. I join in for a while to keep him happy. I couldn't bear a divorce so this is our solution. He gets to play away. But we leave together and stay together.'

The other two nodded. Them too. In other words, to maintain their respectable and ordered life they had all agreed to do something utterly degrading. It's weird what women will do to hang on to love, I thought. Whilst simultaneously wondering if I should confess that we had the lot on tape so if they wanted to blackmail the little cheating gits into a quick and expensive divorce, we could sort the whole thing right now.

But I didn't. Instead we drank wine. The talk moved onto pensions and Radio 2. Swinging parties are so grown up, I thought.

I mentioned all this to Mike as we left in the car half an hour later, footage of the romps safely stashed in the boot. Was this a story? What women will do to save a marriage? The curse of the mid-life crisis on the middle-aged wives? I had some really interesting quotes, I told him. He looked at me in the same way I'd looked at the hostess when she asked me to join her on the sheets. With uncomprehending horror. He shook his head and sighed, 'Cut the bleeding-heart stuff, you're not writing for the fucking *Guardian*. In a tabloid it's: "Bored housewife runs rollercoaster wife-swap sessions in funfair town".

'Look, we've got everything we need from the bedroom. You were useless, by the way. Running out like that mid-orgy. What's wrong? You never been to one before?'

God. Useless at reporting, useless at orgies and now my fake boyfriend was cross with me too.

Mike sped off, lit up and somehow reached for his phone at the same time. 'Newsdesk? Yeah . . . I'm on the Blackpool job . . . Illuminations mate? I've been staring at the black hole of Calcutta all afternoon . . . Right. It's Kiss Me Quick. I've filmed the hostess at work and let's freeze-frame it and put a Blackpool Tower in the strategic place. Shame it's not Paris, we could joke about an Eiffel. Now, do you think a stick of rock joke is taking it too far . . .?'

I got home at 4 am, and was woken by a bunioned foot and then a phone call from my mother.

'So, what have you been up to in the papers?' she said. Still half asleep, I mentioned vaguely I'd been up in Blackpool. Big mistake.

'You were up in Blackpool? That's only up the road from us. Why didn't you come over for tea? We're only an hour away.'

I woke up. I stuttered. I lied. I squirmed guiltily under the duvet. What is the best way to explain you didn't pop home to your mum and dad because you were out pretending to be a swinger? I muttered something about being on an urgent job with a man called Mike, being on a deadline and not really having had the time.

'Mike? Who's Mike?' asked my mother hopefully.

'Married,' I replied.

'Oh,' was her crestfallen response.

'But he was pretending to be my boyfriend,' I added.

'What?'

'Never mind,' I said. 'Look. I've got to go. I have to file by 9 am.'

'Crump?' yelled the News Editor. 'What job you on?'

'TV star's lust for hookers.'

'Good. Good. Crime?'

'House of horrors.'

'Investigations?'

'Rollercoaster wife swaps in funfair town.'

'Good, good. Don't forget the tower joke. Politics?'

'Trying to get Blair on the Belfast Agreement?'

'Oh forget it, Pictures have got Cherie in a swimsuit. That will sail in with a *Titanic* reference and take up Page Three.'

It was three minutes before Conference and tabloidese was flying across the newsroom. I had struggled to tell my mother exactly what I'd been up to the previous day, but summing up incredibly improbable events in incredibly few words is a skill you learn as a tabloid hack.

Tabloids have their own language. Maybe it's because the pages are smaller than the broadsheet papers, or perhaps it's because they have to make room to fit all those pictures of Jordan in her knickers in each day, but tabloidese is a language and a skill peculiar to the red tops.

Forget anything you learned in your grammar lessons at school. There simply isn't the time or space to remember the rules on auxiliary verbs when you've got an orgy to sum up in under eight paragraphs.

Look through a tabloid newspaper and the same basic rules apply to each story. No sentence should ever be longer than twenty words. No headline over six. Sentences are short. Quotes are colourful. And everything is as dramatic as possible.

People, for example, never just 'say' anything. That's dull and stories in tabloids are never dull. So instead people will 'gasp', 'storm', 'rage', 'thunder' or 'sob' their quotes. Tales will be 'shocking', women will be 'stunners' and observers and sources will all be 'outraged'.

This all takes practice to perfect, and after a while tabloid people don't just talk like this in print. They talk like this in the newsroom too.

'Just off to this kiss-and-tell – she's a right stunner,' one will say, with a cheery wave goodbye. Or, there'll be a nod in the canteen queue, ''Ere. Reckon she'll sell the story of her heartache then?' Or a shout from the back of a pub, 'See you all in a jiffy then. This Russell Brand bird's just called and we're all on for that three-in-a-tub lust for Page Three.'

Good tabloidese is not just about dropping every rule you ever learned about sentence construction. Every tabloid hack reads every newspaper and every magazine that's sold on the newsstands, every day. This is so they can build up a precise encyclopaedic knowledge of the love life of every person in the public eye. The skill in constructing a perfect news story is to incorporate every inch of this detail. So, the ideal sentence will not only sum up who the person is and why you should be interested in them, but also give a brief summary of their past relationships. And, if appropriate, breast measurements.

So, Peter Andre becomes, for example, the 'lovelorn ex of randy 32DD glamour girl Jordan'. Hilary Clinton will forever be the 'wife of sex shame ex-President Bill Clinton'. Darren Day will be a 'serial love-rat TV star' until the day he dies, and Ulrika, no matter how often she marries and settles down, the '4×4 Swedish man-eater', with a paragraph or two explaining the latest developments on her cup size.

'Imagine,' advised Crump, 'that you are writing for a four-year-old with a shorter-than-average attention span, a passing interest in world politics, absolutely no memory recall and a total obsession with other people's love lives and bra sizes, and you will get it about right.

'Oh. And try and sum up the whole thing in the first paragraphs, a lot of people only read that far.'

It's quite a skill really, once you realise the amount of thought that goes into it all.

Anyway, on this day I was still struggling with how to use fewer than twenty words to sum up my day in Blackpool in a manner which would not prove too upsetting for my parents, when I learned that I'd got spiked. Again.

Spiking is an old-fashioned term that dates back to the days when papers were produced on typewriters. Copies of all the day's stories would be gathered, before the rejected ones would be cruelly and publicly impaled on a giant metal spike in the centre of the newsdesk. Nowadays your work evaporates with just one computer key; and, so, with a press of the 'delete' button, the seaside orgy-goers had been spared.

The Editor had decided he was bored with it. Again. I suppose he must get a lot of them though.

It was all a bit of a relief to be honest, given that I was facing severe parental enquiries about what exactly I had been doing Up North that was so important I couldn't pop round for tea. I had been wondering how to break the news. I seriously doubted whether my parents would appreciate the technical skill that had gone into getting the story.

I still hadn't plucked up the courage to even confess to my parents that I smoked. Never mind that I had now progressed to smoking in pre-designated areas at wild spouse-trading parties.

I didn't want to spoil the magic. So instead, that night, I said nothing. I merely gave monosyllabic responses to questions and invited no further discussion. How was my day? 'Fine'. Just, 'fine'. There was nothing of interest to report really. Everything was 'fine'.

Yes, I just pretended none of it was happening. That seemed like the best thing to do.

I was also a tiny bit relieved on behalf of the wife-swap wives I'd met. I've often wondered what those women who couldn't face the scandal of divorce would have done if they'd ended up pictured in their knickers in a national newspaper. I wonder if they all still go to Blackpool each year, and still neatly fold their clothes in that kitchen next to the vol-au-vents? I wonder how the hostess's son is getting on at school?

I also wondered, if breaking into movie sets and going swinging didn't hack it, what the hell I was going to have to do to get a story into the paper?

The answer, I was soon to discover, was to really, really piss off Mr Jeremy Paxman.

3

MY PAXO TERROR

And the Art of the Doorstep

A dishevelled blonde figure slunk into the office, shirt tails trailing out behind his jacket, nervously scanning the glass walls of The Editor's lair.

'Brownfinger!' came the shout from the Showbiz Desk.

The Sub-Editing team broke into the trumpet solo from *Goldfinger*, and pointed their imaginary brass section in the direction of the shambling figure who nervously waved at them with a chubby biro-stained hand, begging them to shut up.

'Shhh. He'll hear,' whimpered the stained one.

Crump stood up and delivered the chorus at full volume.

'*Brownfinger . . . He's the man, the man with the shitty touch.*'

The Editor's door burst open. Crump pointed at the cowering figure and completed the chorus.

'*He'll. Fuck. It. Up.*'

Crump directed the stained one towards The Editor's door.

Right on cue came a shriek from behind the glass. 'Get in here. Bring a good explanation!'

'Oh, fuck,' whimpered the man as he went. The Subs made the sign of the cross as he passed.

'Dear old Brownfinger,' sniggered Crump as the condemned man shuffled past. 'Everything he touches turns to crap.

'There was a job last night,' Crump went on, as he held up his cigarettes and signalled a trip to the smoking room. He explained on the way. 'Investigations spent six months setting up a purer-than-pure TV star on this drugs exposé. All Brownfinger had to do was go in with the old camera bag and sit there whilst she hoovers up the coke in front of him. Piece of cake this one, *piece of cake*. The whole thing was almost in the bag. Guaranteed splash. Epic story.

'But we reckoned without Brownfinger, didn't we? She offers a line of coke, Brownfinger says, "Oh, yes please!" and starts bloody snorting it all. On camera. What a twat! Didn't even know what he'd done wrong. Investigations team just sat there watching him as he gets the old nosebag on and the whole thing shoots up his snout.'

Crump looked towards The Editor's office, as the door slammed behind Brownfinger's broken form.

'Whole tape's utterly unusable,' whispered Crump as we passed. 'Key witness right there in the middle, face deep in the evidence. It'll take them years to lure her back again.'

A muted screaming began to emit from behind the glass wall.

'Now, that,' said Crump with a wince, 'is going to be one hell of a bollocking.'

*

The TV star had no idea what was being held on her in the vaults of the newspaper offices. Or how close she'd come to ruin. There are lots of things held in lots of newspaper offices about lots of celebrities. And often they know nothing about it until they see it on a front page.

The relationship between newspapers and celebrities is an odd one. On the plus side, newspapers will give celebrities great big cheques just for having a date with someone, and then put nice photos of them in the paper which are professionally airbrushed so they look like they're *really*, *really* thin.

Being on the telly is brilliant. Bag a job as a primetime star and you get the most ludicrous amount of money for not doing an awful lot, and the most ludicrous amount of freebies. You rarely have to pay for your own drinks any more, people throw goody bags of lovely free things at you constantly and you get sack-fulls of cash to top it all off. You can be handed an entire fly-on-the-wall documentary series, book and pop career just for splitting up with someone. Kerry Katona's made a mint out of this sort of thing for years. She only has to agree to walk past Mothercare holding her stomach and looking wistful in front of a pre-arranged snapper and another cheque's on its way.

There are levels of celebrity. At the top are people like the pop starlet I know who pockets £160,000 a year from a mobile phone firm, just for agreeing to always ensure she's carrying one of their handsets when she gets off a plane, and get photographed by the waiting paparazzi crowd.

On a slightly tackier note – but personally, I always find it funny when I spot this in a magazine – you may also notice an awful lot of soap stars these days swear blind that their favourite place to eat in the whole world is Nando's. Which is odd, when a lot of them can afford The Ivy. The reason for the chicken fascination is because the second you start regularly appearing in a soap, you will be sent an envelope containing a shiny plastic credit card emblazoned with the words 'Friend of Nando's'. This card, it is explained on the back in nice silver letters, enables them, 'and five friends', to eat as much chicken as they like, for free, in any of five continents. Naff, isn't it? But you see them eating in there all the time. Saves them a fortune in poultry.

So that's the freebies side of being a celeb. All good. But you only get all this because of the papers. So to keep their profile high and the job offers coming in they need the papers to keep writing about them. If the papers stop writing about you, stop bothering that you've split up with someone, or that you're pretending to be pregnant, or getting married, or divorced, then you stop being a celebrity. You don't get invited to the nice parties with free booze. You have to buy your own chicken wings like everyone else. *Everybody forgets who you are.* In the end, you're reduced to drumming up publicity by either going on *Celebrity Big Brother*, pretending to be a lesbian, or getting so fat that the papers print a 'Oh my God look at the state of them now' picture, so you can go cash in on an exercise video.

Unfortunately, the papers don't just want to print pictures saying you look thin or that they've spotted you eating in Nando's. They like to print more exciting stuff too. And they're right nosey buggers when it comes to your love life and they want to write all about that too. Particularly if you've been misbehaving . . .

The person they'd turned the spotlight on to at this point was Jeremy Paxman.

Now Paxman, as far as I know, didn't really enjoy many of the fruits of celebrity. He's not a red carpet regular. I don't recall any swimwear shoots in *OK!*. To the best of my knowledge, he always paid for his own chicken. But he was on the telly a lot and was therefore 'a celebrity'. And was therefore, in the tabloid's eyes, fair game when it came to the being nosey bit.

At this precise point in time, Jeremy Paxman stood accused of being a naughty boy. He had, allegedly, been having an affair. Sorry, he had been having a 'sizzling affair' – that's the correct tabloidese and that's how one paper put it at the time. Celebrities in tabloids don't have ordinary affairs, you see. They have sizzling ones, because they sound more exciting.

Anyway, after this accusation was made, all the other papers stopped writing nice things about Jeremy Paxman – like how clever he was, and how good he was at sneering at politicians – and instead they all went and knocked on his door and asked if it was true about the sizzling bit.

Paxo, as yet, hadn't commented. And that, the News Editor had decided, was where I came in.

As a lowly, brainless sludge-like shifter, I wasn't allowed into Conference that day, so I wasn't privy to the exact conversation that took place in the bunker, but I imagine it went something like this:

The Editor: I hear rumours that Jeremy Paxman has had an affair?

News Editor: Yes Gov. A sizzling one, apparently.

The Editor: I see. Tell me, how many times did Paxo ask Michael Howard the same question when he was interviewing him that time?

News Editor: Fourteen, Gov.

The Editor: Great. Go round to Paxo's. And ask him if it's true. Ask him fourteen times.

News Editor: Brilliant idea, Gov.

News Editor exits Conference. And thinks, 'Now, I wonder which one of the reporters is going to be stupid enough to agree to go and do that?'

Crump had winced on my behalf when he overheard the instruction being issued. In fact, he even perused the Investigations Desk for any left over mind-altering drugs which may help, but the cupboard was bare save for some black-market Viagra. That, we decided, may be a touch inappropriate under the circumstances.

War reporting may be seen as front-line, dangerous stuff for hacks, but actually I've always thought that love-life enquiries are far riskier. The *Mirror* once ran a series of articles about Jeremy Clarkson claiming he, too, may have been cavorting on occasion with a lady who was not Mrs Clarkson. Clarkson vociferously denied the scandalous accusations and, when he came face-to-face with the paper's then editor Piers Morgan at a Press Awards party, he promptly started thumping him to try and drive this point home. I was actually there at the time and remember diving under a nearby table as the pair squared up and a six-deep pack of male journalists in tuxedos suddenly swarmed around them shouting 'Finish him!' A short man, I think he was from the *Sun*, tried to intervene, raising his fists and shouting, 'I'm from Newcastle! You better watch out!' for some unknown reason, before Clarkson's fists started flying in a windmill move. He was eventually torn off Morgan by security and everyone went back to the bar to decide who had won the fight. The point I'm making here is that even the most likeable celebrities like Clarkson can get quite cross, and at the poshest of bashes, when you question them about their private life. And Paxman, I think it is fair to point out, can hardly be described as an affable sort.

Paxman. Paxo. Now that man's a tough cookie, isn't he? Bit short tempered and growly? Once started firing off all sorts of angry missives to the bosses of Marks & Spencer just because he didn't feel his underpants were offering up the requisite amount of elasticity and suspension in the undercarriage department. A man who gets angry just putting his knickers on is not a man to cross. In fact, he's so snappy Alan Sugar looks positively Prozac'd up to the gills in comparison.

'Mate,' said Crump, white-faced, as he led me to the pub at 9.15 am and rapped on the door for the bar to be opened early. 'Fourteen times? Paxo? The only possible breakfast for this occasion is an alcoholic one. This is a genuine emergency.'

We both sighed over our double brandy stiffeners. 'You've got a toughie there,' said Crump. In fact, he was so concerned he said he would've come with me for moral support, but he'd just been instructed to spend the rest of his day wearing a pantomime cow outfit. The Editor had decided that was the best incognito way of staking out the Spice Girls, who at the time were holed up in a countryside house in the middle of a dairy farm. Crump was to take the back half, because the photographer insisted he needed the front to take photos. 'How am I meant to smoke?' Crump had wailed as his black and white furry legs were delivered.

Despite Crump's advice and entreaties, I stuck to just the one double brandy for breakfast and left twenty minutes later, whilst I could still see.

'Try and get back early,' added Crump, as he slapped me on the back in farewell. They were all going on a drinking bender that afternoon as soon as he'd finished being a pretend cow. 'I'll square it all with The Editor, don't worry,' he added.

'How?' I asked.

'Investigations just got a job lot of Viagra in, remember?' he said cheerfully. 'Spike that in The Editor's coffee and he won't leave the office until at least 4 pm.'

Which sadly, it occurred to me, as I set off to Oxfordshire, would probably mean The Editor would be in an increasingly agitated mood all morning. Thank God I'd had a stiff one to start the day, too.

All the way along the M40 that morning I panicked.

How the hell was I going to phrase this one?

How was I going to make sure I didn't come back with a Brownfinger result?

Paxo had faced and snarled down the country's toughest.

His CV at this point covered The Troubles, Beirut, that notorious interview with Michael Howard and included a BAFTA and two Royal Television Society awards for Interviewer of the Year. My work so far as a national newspaper journalist consisted of quotes from an actress's pet dog and a swinger. Both unpublished.

I rehearsed the conversation in my head. Even if I had the faintest idea of how to conduct an interview, there was no polite way of putting it, really. Certainly no polite way of putting it fourteen times.

1. Are you having an affair, Mr Paxman?
2. Is it a sizzling one, would you say, Mr Paxman?
3. Have you been having sexual relations, Mr Paxman?
4. This is your starter for ten, Mr Paxman. I have a delicate question concerning your underpants.

Four. That was only four. I'd have to come up with another *ten*.

This was going to be slow and it was going to be painful. And Paxman was going to go absolutely nuts. As I pulled into a slip road near Destination Paxo, I was hyperventilating and seriously thought I was going to vomit over the fluffy dice in my Nissan Micra.

One of the paper's photographers was standing, waiting, in the road – camera in hand – looking at me in surprise.

'You came? Are you s*eriously* going to do this?' he said. The man, Simon, had recently returned from dodging bullets in Kosovo and had just agreed to go off to Iraq the following morning. 'I'd rather be there, to be honest,' he admitted.

I'd been told to ring in to the newsdesk before I started the job.

'You're there then?' said the News Editor. He sounded surprised.

I could barely breathe. 'I'm here,' I whispered, from behind Paxo's wheelie bins. Wishing I had another double brandy as a final meal before facing the Paxman firing squad.

The lawyer came on the phone. 'I need the whole thing on tape,' he said. He sounded surprised I was there too.

'Good luck,' said the lawyer.

'Good luck,' said the News Editor and hung up.

'Good luck,' said the war-hardened snapper. And then hid himself behind a bush.

The only hope for me now, I thought as I started the long trek up the gravel of Paxo's front garden path, was that he wasn't in. Please. *Please*, let him not be in. That way, I could break the sad news to the newsdesk that yes, it *had* been a brilliant idea by The Editor, and yes I'd gone, and yes I'd gone with a tape recorder. And *really* wanted to do it. But dash it. We were foiled because he was out. Let's send someone else tomorrow.

I reached the door. *Let him not be in*. I knocked on the door. *Let him not answer*. I waited. *Let him not open the door*.

Paxman opened the door.

Oh, bollocks.

It's a weird thing being faced with a celebrity. Somebody off the telly. The automatic response is to grin inanely, point at them, perhaps give them a compliment about their hair and then ask for a picture.

I grinned at Paxman. He does have a lovely head of hair, I thought. Then I remembered why I was there and felt my lips stick to my teeth. I think I may have frothed slightly at the mouth.

Paxman, at the best of times, instantly inspires total fear. Is he going to shoot a load of quiz questions at you? Point a camera on you, tell you that you're now live to the nation on *Newsnight* and then ask you about the economy?

Trust me, none of this general feeling of terror improves when you turn up, uninvited, to ask him about rumours of illicit affairs. My knees went.

Paxman was still looking at me, quizzically. I looked back . . . vacantly. My mind had gone totally blank with fear. What the hell was I supposed to be asking? I twitched a bit.

Then I remembered. And nearly fainted. I managed an 'uh' and I held up the tape recorder.

Paxman continued to look at me in confusion. An eyebrow raised. His smile a fraction less friendly. A small child arrived in the background and was ushered away. I had a feeling I was about to face the same fate. I pressed record on my dictaphone, introduced myself and said I was a tabloid journalist.

He stopped smiling.

I asked the question for a first time. Paxman did that 'you're a lump of something on my shoe' sneer he adopts when addressing the worst of the politicians about the worst of their crimes. I asked him the question again. I'd say his expression didn't get any friendlier.

'What's that?' the lawyer was to ask me later, as I played the tape in his office and we heard a loud crunching noise at this particular point in my Paxman encounter. That, I replied, was the sound of my feet being frogmarched down the path, as Paxo grabbed me by the shoulders and started escorting me off his property, round about question four. The rate of crunching suggested I was moving quite quickly, remarked the lawyer with interest. The noise was punctured with barked variations from Paxman on the 'go away' and 'bye' theme.

Really, when your interview subject has you in a shoulder grip, it's perhaps time to terminate the interview, but with The Editor's missive firmly in mind, I kept bleating the damn question. I remember counting on my fingers behind my back, the third time, the fourth time, the fifth . . . crunch, crunch. The sixth. Luckily he had a long drive.

The thirteenth time was a whimper, pathetically delivered from the garden gate in the direction of the letterbox; by this point Paxman had retreated into his house. He was, I think it was safe to say, really, *really*, not pleased to see me. A slammed door was his final response.

I asked the final question, the fourteenth, in the general direction of the still vibrating front door, listened for a few seconds in case a miracle occurred and he re-emerged at the door with a smile, wanting to invite me in and tell all, and then fled.

I looked round for the snapper, who I naively imagined had been waiting and capturing the whole heroic thing. He'd completely vanished.

I found him back in his car, smoking a cigarette and reading the *Sun*.

'Did you get all that on film then?' I asked.

'God, no,' said the man who'd followed Serbian troops. 'I can't believe you actually rang the doorbell. I turned round the second he answered the door and went straight back to my car. Are you *completely* insane?'

I called the newsdesk to see what they thought. And to see if I was still employed. There was a vaguely stunned silence as I reported that I had, in fact, gone through with it, and a muffled conversation as my efforts were relayed to the room. I could hear the News Editor saying something along the lines of, 'actually gone and done it'.

Then I could hear The Editor in the background. He sounded quite distant. I presumed he was still confined to his office desk.

'Did Paxman actually answer the question?' I heard his distant rasp.

I started getting that hyperventilating feeling again.

'No . . .' I ventured, hesitantly, to the News Editor.

'No,' was relayed to The Editor.

Another distant rasp. 'Tell her to go back and ask him again.'

Paxman once famously asked the notorious love-rat Cecil Parkinson, 'You're the chairman of a fertiliser firm. How deep is the mess you're in at present?' It occurred to me that knocking on his door and asking the affair question a fifteenth time would land me in fairly deep mess myself. I asked the war-veteran photographer what he thought I should do. He shook his head and returned to the *Sun*.

I turned round and went straight back to my Nissan Micra and stayed there staring at the dice. 'He must have gone out,'

I lied to the News Editor half an hour later. I was probably fooling no one.

'Wait there in case he comes back and fancies a chat,' he replied, hanging up. I hid up the road for ten hours, reporting every half hour that, 'He hasn't come back yet. Can I go now?' And being told, firmly, no.

'Look, I'm sure he'd love a little chat. A chance to set the record straight. He's a journalist. He'll understand,' said the News Editor each time I rang. 'Just wait there a bit longer and see what he says when he comes home.'

The scars are there for life. I haven't been able to watch *University Challenge* since without breaking out into a cold sweat and still have to switch off *Newsnight*. It gives me hives.

Paxman has clearly picked up lots from politicians over the years. After all, I was still none-the-wiser as to whether any of the affair stuff was true or not.

But there was a reward. I wasn't fired. And as I rang at midnight, 'Congratulations. You're finally in print,' said the News Editor.

My 'interview' – consisting of my bleated questions, in which I noticed I had called Paxman 'sir' fourteen times, in the manner of a terrified schoolgirl – had made it in. Years of training, wishing, dreaming and begging to become a journalist and I'd finally made it into a national newspaper. My first byline. Okay, so all the interview subject had really said to me was 'Go away'. But I was, finally, in print.

'You've got a week of shifts,' slurred the News Editor, who had clearly joined what I later heard had turned into a fourteen-hour drinking session in the pub, as The Editor had failed to emerge from his office for the entire day. 'As a treat, in the morning you're on kiss-and-tells.'

As I started the engine I could just hear the distant cheers from the pub as the News Editor added: 'As The Editor would probably say right now, let's see what you can make stand up.'

4

MY LUSTFEST WITH LEMMY

And the Art of the Kiss-and-Tell

So. Work wise I was on my way. A whole week of work promised. Commitment. Much more than any man was promising me at the time. In fact the News Editor was the only man in my life who returned my calls.

I didn't care about my abject failure on the man front, though. For here, in my mid-twenties, I was still in the first stage of singledom. The 'Not Bothered' stage.

My poor parents would ring each week with reports of school friends who had made better career choices than me and were now leading wholesome, fulfilled lives with adoring families.

'Remember Emma, the girl down the road who you used to walk to school with?' Mum would say. 'Two years younger than you, wasn't she? She became a vet. She's engaged now.'

Or, 'Jill. Remember Jill from primary school? Yes, you do, you did the Three-Legged Race together that year, remember? You came third. I saw her out on the market last week. Two children she's got now. Works in a lovely office. She was asking how you were getting on?'

How was I getting on? Well pretty badly, if you're going by the scoring system of a small Lancashire town. Engagement, marriage, birth. These are the measures of life's success, and I was failing.

That's the problem with small towns. Everyone knows you. Every visit to the newsagent, every transaction at Tesco's and my parents would be expected to deliver a progress report on my life. And my poor parents had no big white dresses, vicars or joyous news from my ovaries to offer. They even had to resort to ordering my tabloid paper from a newsagent in a village four miles away, just in case anyone local saw them buying it and picked up on the fact that, actually, their daughter spent her time being shouted at by people off the telly.

'Ah, she's still single,' I imagined them saying when asked for updates, as everyone from my old school settled down.

'Tracy. You know Tracy. Tracy who got detention that time for sniffing Tippex off her school shirt, do you remember her? Pregnant she is! Lovely husband.' Even Tippex Tracy found love and added to her family tree, whilst I remained rootless in London.

Quite honestly though, I don't know how they'd all found the time. Even if I did meet anyone, I just couldn't see how I would fit the whole 'Having a Boyfriend' thing into my timetable right now. Dating, you see ... it just all takes so much bloody effort.

You have to spend a fortune on pulling clothes for a start. Tight skirts and high heels that ram your feet onto tiptoes, so you spend the evening unable to breathe with cramping feet. But instead of wincing and sulking that your feet hurt, you have to smile coquettishly, hold in your stomach and spend hours doing all that hair twirling and eye-catching with strangers in bars.

Then, maybe, *maybe*, if you're lucky, after an agonising two hours of this, someone may ask for your number. Then there's a whole week of waiting for them to ring and wondering if you should ring them. All that kerfuffle of pretending to ignore them when they first call, or waiting for an acceptable amount of time before returning a text. And wondering what to say. What to write. How to flirt yet not look too easy. And spending hours with your mates trying to analyse what their last text meant.

Then if you succeed, if you finally get A Date, there's more worry to come. Another pulling outfit to buy. Then a torturous evening in which you have to worry about not getting drunk, remembering to ask the 'correct' date questions and not reveal anything stupid about your past pathetic love life. And then panicking about whether it's okay to kiss them. And if you should sleep with them or not.

If you actually ever get to the sleeping with them bit, there's more Hell unleashed. More rules. More clothes shopping. Waxing.

Get through that and then you're in for at least three months of panic about whether he's committed and if it's okay to call him your boyfriend. And then weeks of being on tenterhooks worrying if he's going to dump you, or introduce you to his mother, followed by several months or years of wondering why he hasn't proposed yet, like Tippex Tracy's man has.

Fair play to everyone back home for making it to the altar, but frankly, I just didn't have the time for all this. I was too busy breaking into film sets and annoying TV presenters. I just couldn't fit it all in.

But, like I say, I wasn't bothered. Your twenties are an age when it's fine to be single. In a city, it's normal to be single. I was too young to be anything but single in a city. Settling down in your twenties was a ludicrous notion, I thought. Frankly, I would decide, as I spent evenings with my other single girlfriends in London, those girls from home, with their constant stream of fiancés and children, were poor misguided fools. They were throwing their lives away. They should be concentrating on their careers, like me.

Okay, I went along to a few weddings at the time, but I'd feel superior as I sat alone on my church pew. I would shake my head during the service, privately thinking that it would never work out, because they were both 'so young'. I'd stay just to drink at their free bar before seeing if I could be bothered trying to cop off with the Best Man.

In church I would listen as the vicar did his 'do you . . .?' bit at the front, and then snigger silently as the bride said she'd never sleep with anyone else but her husband again. 'At twenty-five!' I'd whisper smugly to my single friends afterwards. 'Crazy fools.'

'It was a lovely service,' I'd tell my mum when I got home.

'But I'm afraid you've got a bit of a wait ahead of you before you see me in a gown. I want a career.'

Because I may not be married, I may not have 'made it' by the standards of my Lancashire roots, but I wasn't a failure. I'd just been promised a week's work in newspapers. And in the tabloid world, that was pretty damn close to a career. I was a success. Right now. That's all I wanted.

I entered the newsroom fresh from my Paxman mauling expecting applause and praise. Perhaps, I had daydreamed that morning, I may even get an ovation.

I got silence. No one gave a damn that I'd spent the previous day dicing with Paxo. In newspapers, you're only as good as your next story.

We were down to four competing shifters now. The shifter who'd stood, ignored, on Ulrika's doorstep for a week had never been invited back. Another had been dropped the previous week. I was glad – he'd been the one with the phials who was writing 'Exclusive!' on my first day. I'd seen him as the staunchest competition. He'd written the most beautiful copy and was covered in awards from his local paper. But fortunately for me he also had a mild form of Tourettes, which at times of stress manifested itself as a twitch. Once he popped, he could not stop, and I heard from the other four shifters that a key phone interview had gone wrong as the poor man fought to gain control of his head and the receiver. Of course, being caring sorts, the competing shifters had all conspired to make absolutely sure that the News Editor had been called over at the precise time of the attacks. Unfortunately, as it was a condition that came on during stress, tabloid life ensured another attack would soon be on its way. He had eventually been fired after being sent on a doorstep to see someone from *The Bill.* He completely terrified the woman inside by mutely convulsing on her doorstep. She slammed the door in his face and called the police. We other shifters silently revelled in his demise and our twitch-free heads as it put us one step closer to getting that job.

I saw the Tourettes guy years later on a red carpet as part of a press pack, brandishing a microphone as George Michael came into view and the pack surged forward. He started to twitch at precisely the wrong moment as George started to say something and, I fear his career may have abruptly ended there as well.

So then there were four. Four people after that main prize. And as I approached my seat I was shot down with a glare from the hot favourite. The man who had already proved so ruthless he was now going by the nickname Robohack.

Robohack was blessed with an open and honest face – a massive advantage for a tabloid journalist as it makes it much easier to con people into trusting you. He was on his eighth shift and proving utterly devoid of emotion. He was a story-gathering machine. He never tired. He would stop at nothing to get the story. Wherever Robohack had trained, it was clearly a little more hardcore than my Lancashire shorthand course.

As I picked up the paper that morning from my local newsagents, I noticed Robohack had just got the front page story. It was a colourful tabloid tale of love. A boy meets girl story about a TV star and her new beau which had run under a headline mentioning a 'frantic cocaine-and-sex session'.

It contained, I'd had to grudgingly admit, a impressive amount of detail. Like precisely where the pair had met. What drugs they'd bought. What hotel they'd gone to. What they'd said, done and shoved up their noses there, together with a precise analysis of what the TV star was now thinking and feeling about the whole incident. Given that neither the TV star, nor the TV presenter she'd romped with, had given any interviews about the whole thing there was a remarkable amount of information there. And Robohack had been able to approach the News Editor the previous day and assure him and the lawyers it was all, 'copper-bottomed, legalled and watertight'.

So how had he done it? Well, it was by using a method that had never been covered on my training course. He'd got the lot, it emerged, by finding, wooing, then bedding the best mate of the female TV star. During their late night romantic meetings, the champagne by the side of the bed covered by expenses, he'd carefully tucked a tape recorder under the pillow. Eventually, the post-coital conversation had turned to her famous friend.

'What's your mate been up to?' Robohack would murmur as he lay stroking his lover's face. And, with the tape whirring away under her pillow, she would tell. The poor girl hadn't realised she was actually dictating a front page story for a national newspaper until the day Robohack casually asked if she was 'free for lunch?' and she turned up at the restaurant to find a legal letter served as a starter by her 'boyfriend'.

'You've just been photographed coming in,' said Robohack,

gesturing to a snapper who was positioned outside the door. 'Now,' he said, pushing a piece of paper towards her. 'Every conversation we've had in bed about your friend has been taped. This is a transcript and all the quotes are going in tomorrow's paper. We can say they came from you and run them under your picture and give your name. Or sign this legal affidavit in front of you to say the quotes are all correct, and your name will be kept out of it and we'll just call you a "friend". So, which it is to be?'

She signed. And Robohack got his splash. He'd also stayed and calmly finished his lunch and had a glass of champagne, before returning to the office. After all, he was celebrating.

Paxo had made it in too, but to an inside page right at the back of the paper. I'd flicked through for ages until I finally found it behind another spread on Jennifer Ellison (32DD).

'Oh . . . there you are . . . oh, bad luck,' said Robohack as I sat down. 'Hey, maybe if you try and get an actual quote from someone next time? I've looked at your interview attempts and all they ever seem to say is fuck off.'

'Fuck off,' I told him.

And realised I was going to have to step up my game. Even Paxo was not going to be enough for a career here.

Anne held a phone aloft. 'It's a Gaffers. Line three,' she announced. There was general silence, muted tuts and some groans.

Crump looked up momentarily, bored, then gave in and signalled he'd take the call. 'Another bloody kiss-and-tell on Dean Gaffney from *EastEnders*,' he sighed, as he swept the back legs of his nicotine-stained cow costume to the floor to make room for a notepad and pen. The cow stunt, incidentally, had made two lines at the top of page nine under the headline, 'Not a-moo-sed, says Scary'.

There followed a brief conversation. 'Hello love? Yes, Robbie Jackson the road sweeper, yes I know him. You slept with him, did you? What did he get up to then? Oh. Not a threesome then? Any lesbionic action? No? Well, to be honest then it isn't really worth it, darling. We had him attempt a fivesome last week.' There was another pause before he told her to perhaps try and get photos next time, that she was to ring *immediately* if there were ever two girls involved or 'one of the Mitchells' and then he put the phone down with a sigh.

'We used to buy in the Gaffers tales for £2,000 a pop,' Crump said. 'But we've had that many, we've run out of Well'ard jokes now.

'Right then,' he rallied, grabbing his wallet. 'You're on kiss-and-tells this week, I gather? Pub's open. Come on. Let me tell you how it works.'

So that morning I was educated in the art of the tabloid kiss-and-tell.

It may never get displayed in an art gallery, but writing a tabloid kiss-and-tell is undoubtedly a specialised art form. A strange art, sometimes an unsavoury one, indeed, a morally dubious one at times, but an art form nonetheless. A tabloid staple, the kiss-and-tell is harder to write than you'd think.

It's often a case of making a one fact story – 'I got to third base with someone off the telly' – stretch to a racy headline, two pages of copy and a photo shoot. Not bad, considering that quite often the whole thing had been over in less than a minute.

First up, said Crump over a restorative Guinness, a few lessons in the correct tabloidese for the occasion. 'No one ever just has "sex". Sex is for ordinary people. Ordinary people who don't have to report about it in newspapers the next day.'

For the purposes of tabloids, people are required to have one thousand different styles of wildly exciting bedroom activities. So they have the 'romps' or 'sizzling romps' that we've covered, or, even better, 'torrid romps and lust-fuelled sessions' and 'shenanigans', 'wild nights of passion', 'red-hot love affairs', and 'kinky', 'swinging', 'fetishist', 'PVC-laden, bondage-loving, bullwhip-branding, rubbertastic, ooh! Ouch! Wow! Wham! Bam! Sordid nights of spanking orgy shame.'

If it's someone really inventively sluttish like Russell Brand, you can get away with putting the entire list in the one story.

'Second,' said Crump, 'fuck the facts and make it fit. Just write it.' In other words, if the encounter turned out to be incredibly dull, you should add a helping hand and just liven it up for them. Nine times out of ten, the kiss-and-tellee will report they were 'drunk and don't really remember anything' but Crump informed me that, 'This is no barrier to writing a full, frank and detailed account. Because in that case, you give that what is known as a "bit of tabloid top-spin".'

Which is, he added, code for simply making it all up.

Kiss-and-tells tend to be done on men. Single, young, silly, drunk men. And these men, when they are the subject of these kiss-and-tells, rarely object to the facts being fiddled with. As long as it's flattering.

Think about it. You're a single guy and you open the paper to read that a drunken romp with a former conquest you can barely remember is now being breathlessly recounted to the nation. A 'stunner', airbrushed and coquettish in designer knickers, is exclaiming about how well endowed and fabulous you are as a lover and how you are a total Love God with incredible stamina and performance. Which is odd, as all you can remember is pulling some ropey old slapper in a club before falling asleep.

Lawsuits are few and far between. 'Trust me,' said Crump. 'No bloke will ever, ever, sue or complain at being branded an absolute stud in the papers.'

Sometimes the resulting descriptions of bedroom shenanigans were so good that the celebrity, far from being outraged at the invasion of his privacy, would actually ring in person to thank us afterwards. One *Coronation Street* actor was even polite enough to send a written thank you note for one kiss-and-tell article's descriptions of his prowess, which was nice of him. He did point out in a polite postscript that he wasn't sure that he had actually ever met the young lady in question. But, he added, this was 'a mere detail' and he had no intention whatsoever of suing as the article had been 'absolutely brilliant' for his love life and ladies were now throwing themselves at him in Manchester nightclubs in the mistaken belief they were in for 'hours of rampant passion'.

Thirdly. Don't let anything surprise you. 'Always ask them if "anything unusual" went on,' counselled Crump. 'And whatever madness they tell you, try to sound bored. Leave a long silence. That way they'll panic, think they're being dull, and always tell you a bit more of the juicy stuff.'

This last tip really works, actually. One young lady who had just romped with an A-List Hollywood star, panicked during my strategic silence and threw in an entirely unexpected line about how he'd enjoyed throttling himself with his tie. Unfortunately the lawyers never allowed that one through, although every time he appears in films in any formal neckwear I get uncontrollable giggles and have to leave the cinema.

Next, you've got to sort out the fee, counselled Crump. Women don't just sit down and tell you all about earth-shattering nights with celebrity Love Gods for free, after all. Money is usually the motivator. Although in print, obviously, when explaining what the young lady is doing there, in her knickers, telling us all about her former lover, it's traditional to use the term 'heartache' and say she's doing it because she wants the world to see 'the truth behind his showbiz image'. Well, that's what we always wrote anyway. It looks so much better than, 'Well I just rang up and tried to flog it because it struck me it might be worth a bit of cash.'

Newspapers, pointed out Crump, all carry phone numbers urging you to 'ring in if you've got a story', claiming you'll get a large wad of cash as a result. Surprisingly, lots of people do actually ring into these. At least once a week, a tremulous female voice would emerge from the end of the phone, ringing in to say she'd slept with someone famous and could she now have some money?

The answer for the fair maiden on the phone is dependent on a few things, explained Crump. First up, who have they slept with? There is a sliding scale of financial reward depending on the star. Bag an A-Lister, in formal neckwear or not, and you could be talking about a sizeable deposit on a new house. Particularly if the star was married. Rebecca Loos got at least a penthouse out of Beckham. Bag a TV reality star, from, say, a *Big Brother* series from three years ago, and you're lucky to get your bus fare home.

There were some regulars. I remember that during the early years of my career, we would expect a call from Alicia Douvall most weeks. The surgically swelled model had started off quite strongly and got a lot of cash for early kiss-and-tells on Dwight Yorke and Mick Hucknall and continued the trend with tales of some admirably athletic nights with Shaggy and Simon Cowell, but her stock rapidly dropped when she started ringing in with Dane Bowers, and by the time she started on the boyband Blue, she was barely covering a month's rent.

Crump warned me about this sort of thing and counselled never to promise an amount until I'd checked exactly how famous the girl's co-star in the kiss-and-tell was. I remember we always had to be especially careful with Jodie Marsh, too; another regular over the years. Particularly when she started getting down to ex-Corrie stars.

'With all of these kiss-and-tells, if you have to Google the lover to find out who they are, then it's probably only worth a few hundred,' said Crump.

Next question, Crump went on. 'Is the girl doing the kiss-and-tell a "looker"? You can add at least another £5,000 onto the price if she's going to look good in her knickers and bra, and be willing to pose in a nice big picture in the paper that will take up two pages.' There's a sliding scale of descriptions for the girls. A 'stunner' is a girl who can be used for a full lingerie shoot with minimal clothes and airbrushing. 'Pretty' is applied to those who are perhaps best presented in the paper fully dressed, or largely hidden under a fur rug and shadows. 'Attractive' is usually a head and shoulders shot with a specialist makeover artist involved. 'If they're ugly just put down their hair colour, gloss over their looks and describe them as "heartbroken", advised Crump. 'Don't spend too much time on them. If they can't pose in their knickers they'll probably get spiked anyway.'

And finally, could she prove it? A photo or a stream of text messages was often enough. One person went even further and had shaved off a few locks of their partner's pubic hair as they slept, which they thoughtfully brought along for the shoot. 'I thought you could test it for DNA,' they had said. We assured them the full set of photos and the video recording was more than enough. There was no need to bring clippings.

Anyway, these were all valuable points that I was to need in the future. For I was to attend many kiss-and-tells over the years. Incidentally, I attended so many that at one point my neighbours knocked on my door to confront me and accuse me of being a prostitute. Me exiting the house in various rubber outfits at odd times of the day and night had been bad enough they said, but the loud conversations on my mobile phone as I walked down the communal stairs in the mornings were 'outrageous'.

Turns out my discussions with the newsdesk had been misconstrued. You can see where they were coming from. The previous day I'd trotted out the door yelling: 'So it's ten thousand for full sex and twenty for anything unusual, but anything less, shall we say just three?'

*

I always found kiss-and-tells fascinating to do – the fact that someone could be so coldly calculating to sell something so intimate.

Not all went well though. I was once sent on a 'saucy photo shoot' to mark the thirtieth anniversary of the Joy of Sex with one of the original female models. We'd been briefed for a 'stunner' and the knicker selection was purchased accordingly. Turned out the poor girl's pictures from the model agency were three decades and about five stone out of date. She was sitting, bewildered and naked, on a bed when I saw her, spiritedly trying to get a thigh into one of the thongs. I don't think she'd waxed since the original launch. The photographer and PR were convulsed in horrified giggles when I got there, and in the end it was my job to walk in with a straight face and calming manner to suggest the poor straining lass perhaps wore the duvet instead.

In time I was to learn to take a disposable razor and a large fur rug on every job. Just in case.

Anyway, in the end no airbrushing, no fact fiddling and no top-spin and no body-covering props were needed for my first ever kiss-and-tell.

It was the mysterious case of Lemmy from Motörhead and his three depraved days of 'sex-slave lust' with a 32 DD *Playboy* model stunner from Newcastle on Tyne.

It provided a textbook example of kiss-and-telling that I was never able to match again.

'The Editor's in a foul mood,' Crump had confirmed that morning, post-Guinness, after he emerged, a broken man, from Conference. The Editor, I was starting to realise, was in a foul mood most mornings. In fact, the reporters would run a book on how quickly he would blow his temper after arriving in the office. The stopwatch started from the moment he opened the doors, and ended with his first bellowed expletive.

The trick, I quickly learned, was to look incredibly busy whenever he came round. Experienced hacks would dive for a phone whenever they saw the bunker door open and pretend to be on a call, so they looked like they were busy story-gathering as he whirled by. A more advanced option, to be used in extreme emergencies, was to pretend to be on the phone and have a speed-dial button set to their own mobile number. They would hit the speed-dial as The Editor approached and cradle one receiver under their chin, pretending to have an earnest conversation, and then ask their imaginary call to 'please hold' as the second phone began to trill on their desk. This way it looked like they were in the middle of one story with another one coming through, and couldn't possibly have time to have an argument with The Editor or be sent on an impossible job.

Being an idiot shifter, I still hadn't figured this out, so I merely stared, open-mouthed as I saw The Editor for the first time. His bunker door burst open and with a yell of 'imbeciles!' he was on the newsroom floor. As phones suddenly started ringing across the newsroom, the timid ginger shifter to my right and I just sat and gawped. Big mistake. We were sitting ducks for a bollocking.

The first expletive came precisely twenty-three seconds later. The Editor stormed past the set of bowed heads on the reporters' desk and stopped at the silent shifters' desk.

Luckily, the ginger one got it.

'Well?' bellowed The Editor. 'What do you think? Is it better short?'

'Short . . . ?' he spluttered.

'Yes. *Short.* Does she look better with it short?' shrieked The Editor.

'It?' he whimpered. 'With a short what?'

The office winced collectively.

'The hair,' said The Editor, slowly. '*She's cut her hair.*'

A phone rang. I dived on it. 'Yes,' I gasped thankfully into the receiver. 'Yes, oh yes, how can I help?'

It was over for Ginger. He was lost. We all knew it. I was desperately thankful for Crump's advice in the pub earlier that week. Read every day's paper from cover to cover before you ever set foot in a tabloid office, and have an opinion ready on every story just in case The Editor approaches you and starts firing random questions like this. I was guessing The Editor was referring to Posh Spice, who'd made Page Three of that day's papers for cutting her hair.

Ginger had still been casually reading his papers, over a leisurely coffee. He grasped wildly at a newspaper in front of him. Sadly for him it was the *Financial Times,* which hadn't covered the event. 'Sorry,' he started. 'Sorry, I've not read everything yet . . .'

I could see The Editor turning puce. He leaned close to the shifter, like the scene from *Alien* where Sigourney Weaver gets sniffed by the monster.

'Not read the papers,' he repeated. He turned to address the office. 'Oh dear, he's not read the fucking papers . . .'

The office held its breath and fell silent. I was vaguely

aware of some reader wittering down the phone at me about a coupon for flower seeds and demanding some information. I had no idea what to do with her, but didn't speak. Now was not the time to break the silence with a petunia enquiry.

'Of course you mean Posh?' started Robohack, from the other side of the desk, unveiling that day's *Mirror* with a flourish. He smirked at Ginger and leaned in conspiratorially to The Editor. 'Better long, I reckon. I still would though. Bet I could make her smile.'

Smart-arse bastard, I thought. Wishing I'd thought to do the same.

The Editor drew away from the Ginger's face and shouted over his shoulder to Robohack as he stalked towards his bunker. 'Good lad! Now. Full hair analysis. The long and the short of it. Which is better? Two pages. With analysis. Ring Nicky Clarke. Duncan Goodhew. And,' he yelled as he swept back into his office, 'Peter Stringfellow.'

'And you, Ginger Spice,' he yelled, coming out again and pointing at Ginger, who was still open mouthed, 'You're fired!'

Of course, we were all terribly sympathetic to the poor departing shifter's face. But, pond life that we were, we smirked with relief behind his back as he left. Another rival had left the building. One less rival for that staff job.

'Look, don't take it to heart,' the News Editor told Ginger as he left. 'Try again in a few weeks. He's just in a foul mood today.'

We never saw him again.

The Editor's mood was only partly brought on by Ginger not knowing the exact state of Posh Spice's follicles at any given moment, he was also still a little pent up from his desk confinement the previous day. But what had really upset him was that the newspaper had just killed his donkey.

The paper had been running a 'Save the Donkey' campaign, which had gone a little wrong. They'd managed to rescue an abused donkey from certain death, paid thousands in vet's fees and then sent the grateful creature to a top-of-the-range sanctuary, where after three months of loving care and mange removal treatment, he'd trotted out for a triumphant photo shoot of his 'new', 'improved', 'cor, what a stunner' donkeytastic self. Or, 'Look at the ass on that!' as the headline intended to put it.

Tragically, the reporter assigned to the donkey exclusive was Brownfinger. He had been so busy calling the newsdesk to report that he'd finished the story and everything had gone really well, that he'd accidentally run over the donkey in his car on the way out. The donkey had died instantly. Brownfinger. Everything he touches. Turns to shit.

Another two-page story was needed and it was needed in the next half hour.

'The story cupboard is bare,' confided Crump urgently as the seconds ticked towards Conference. 'I've rung Jodie Marsh but she had a quiet night in last night. There was no one in Stringfellows, not even Gaffers. Ulrika's gone to *OK!* with the latest bloke and none of my hookers have recognised anyone off the telly this week. All I've got is this bird who's just rung in saying she's been bedded by Lemmy from Motörhead. You may as well take her. She's yours. Seriously. Get something good though, or we're all out of a job by teatime.'

So, my career, the entire paper, and indeed the entire nation's reading pleasure, was now resting on Lemmy from Motörhead. The tattooed monster of rock with the mutton-chops facial hair. A man who was three years older than my dad.

'Come on, Lemmy. Do it for us,' whispered Crump, as he shuffled over to my desk. 'Here's the bird's number. Don't forget to ask her if he did anything really unusual. And try and get a lesbian angle if you can. The Editor *loves* lesbians. They always go in.'

An hour later I put the phone down, exhausted. The conversation with a breathless Miss Julie had started with the words, 'Well, Lemmy tied me to the bed for three days whilst dressed in Himmler's Nazi uniform. Is that any good?'

Crump, listening in on speakerphone, sat up from his customary position of hunched despair, and stared. 'Anything *really* unusual?' he scribbled on a notepad.

'Oh yes,' revealed Miss Julie. 'There was as a matter of fact.'

'He tied you to the bed for *three days*?' I had queried, whilst dutifully noting it all down in shorthand and trying to sound bored, as instructed. 'Didn't you get cramp?' I added, on a purely practical note.

'Oh no,' she said. 'He untied me every few hours so I could go off and have a cup of tea.'

How very gentlemanly, I thought, glad to hear there was genuinely a softer side to the man behind 'Bastards', 'Snake Bite Love', 'Orgasmatron' and 'Iron Fist'. The man who liked to sing, 'love me like a reptile, I'm gonna sink my fangs in you' had clearly been brought up well by his mum after all.

But anyway. Enough of chivalrous tea-serving. 'Sorry, did you say something about vintage Nazi fetish wear borrowed from Himmler?' I queried. 'As in Himmler the mass-murdering head of the Gestapo?'

'Oh yes,' said Miss Julie. In fact Lemmy had a whole bedroom full of uniforms which included Himmler's little set, she confided. 'It was complete with leather boots and a cap. He always said he liked the outfits.'

This, confirmed Crump, who was listening intently, qualified as 'unusual'. 'What does she look like?' he mouthed. A two-handed gesture at chest level indicated I should be asking for some measurements.

'So Julie. Erm, we might want you to do some modelling shots for us . . . glamour maybe? Have you done anything like that before?' I asked.

'Oh, I'm a *Playboy* model,' she purred in a seductive manner, as only those personally selected and trained by Hugh Hefner can. Crump was giving a wild thumbs up in the background, 'A stunner!' he whispered. 'A genuine Hef-approved stunner.'

'Lesbians?' he scrawled hopefully on his pad, and shrugged understandingly when the answer came back negative. 'Can't have everything, I suppose,' he mouthed. 'Ask what he did to her in the Himmler cap.'

'So, Julie, back to the love romps then,' I continued. 'What happened after that nice cup of tea?'

'Well, Lemmy would stride out of the bedroom and bark something in a German accent. Like, "On your kneez *fräulein*. I vant to haf my vicked vay viz you,"' said Julie. Her German accent was pretty good. 'Then he ordered me to get undressed.'

By now her *Playboy* pictures had been found, which proved undressing was also something she was very good at. They were printing out at Crump's desk, who was goose-stepping joyfully around me by now, exclaiming, 'We hav vayz of making ziss vork.'

'Right,' I said calmly, trying to look like I dealt with German-speaking rock stars doing heavy petting in fetish gear on a daily basis and frankly, found the whole thing a bit dull. 'Now, he asked you to get undressed? So what were you wearing at this point?' I asked, in answer to Crump's hastily scribbled instruction which had just been slapped on my desk.

'Black rubber,' came the answer. Crump nodded approvingly. 'Danke schoen,' he said.

'Lemmy told me I was his sex slave and he could do what he liked with me,' added Julie. 'Is this the sort of thing you wanted? Sorry about the lesbians.'

'Oh it's all jolly good, don't worry about the lezzas, I may still be able to make it all work,' I confirmed. 'And what happened then?'

'Oh, then we had sex on the couch, over the couch, on the kitchen floor, on the table, on the stairs, then in the shower . . .'

I was struggling to keep up in shorthand. God knows how she did it in the flesh.

'So how long did that all last?' I wondered, looking with a new-found respect at the pictures of Lemmy, which had just been printed out alongside Julie's.

'About ten hours,' said Julie. Crump kissed Lemmy's moustachioed chops.

'And then Lemmy said he wanted more. Even I thought it was a bit strange, but it was absolutely brilliant,' Julie concluded.

'Excellent,' I said. 'Excellent. Yes, well . . . Well done. This may be good enough. Anything else you can remember at all?' I added.

'Well, he had a bullwhip too. Oh, do you think this is good enough to make it in? I hope so,' said Miss Julie.

'Evidence?' Crump had written on a Post-it note which he slammed on the computer – just in case Lemmy should ever object to anyone saying he was an absolute stud who could keep a rubber-suited *Playboy* model on the edge of tremulous ecstasy for the entire length of an average working day, fuelled by just one cup of tea.

'Oh, yes. We videoed it all if it helps,' breathed Julie.

Crump let out a howl of ecstasy. Presumably a not too dissimilar howl to the noises Miss Julie was making during her tea parties with Lemmy. He then ran triumphantly into The Editor's office, brandishing a picture of Miss Julie aloft as he did so. It was, The Editor decided two minutes later, good enough to make it in.

I'd finally got some quotes in the paper. 'Lemmy roped me to the bed for three days of lust', Miss Julie purred in the headline.

Proofs – or print-outs of each newspaper story – are displayed in the centre of the newsroom after the Sub-Editors have cut and edited the words to fit the space. There was a queue of men who gathered around to read the exploits of Lemmy that afternoon, which were skilfully wrapped around Miss Julie's chest and contained phrases like, 'If he ever gives up rock 'n' roll, he could certainly have a career as a blue-movie star' and 'Lemmy's eyes were on stalks when he saw me. He was so impressed that he even put down his bottle of Jack Daniel's for a few seconds.'

Many of the men were half Lemmy's age and read the story with low, approving whistles. Julie's photo was passed around to respectful nods.

Just as a precaution, we rang Mr Lemmy's lawyer to read the story to him. The office fell silent as I read. 'Then sir,' I said to him, respectfully, solemnly, 'the young lady claims that your client slapped her bottom, carried her into the bedroom, threw her onto the bed and slid her out of her outfit. Which was, she notes, fashioned from black rubber. We then intend to quote her, claiming that your client, whilst drinking hard liquor and wearing Nazi fetish gear, then "made love for 10 hours".'

There was a silence, I was asked to repeat the bullwhip brandishing bit again as he took notes, then the lawyer requested Julie's vital statistics and hair colour and politely said he needed a brief consultation with his client. Ten minutes later he called back. 'Mr Lemmy says it'll be fine,' he said.

I had just got my first ever double-page spread in the paper. 'One-all,' I smirked at Robohack, who'd had a fruitless day avoiding phone calls from his ex-girlfriend.

'Fuck off,' he replied.

The day after publication however, we heard from the solicitor again. In fact, I received the first and only legal letter of my career.

As the correction ran in full under the heading *Lemmy –*

An Apology, it's perhaps best to recreate it here, too. So every-thing's nice and legal and above board. And Lemmy doesn't feel the need to come round and thrash me with a bullwhip until I say I'm sorry. Here it is:

> Lawyers for wild rock star Lemmy have furiously complained about a scurrilous story in last week's news-paper about his sex life.
>
> We told how the 55-year-old Motörhead rocker hand-cuffed his lover Julie Wilson to the bed for a three-day sex and bondage session. Mr Lemmy's lawyer Alexis Grower said: 'It was NOT three days and she was NOT handcuffed to the bed. It was SEVEN days and she was HUNG from the CEILING.'

I am, once again, happy to put the record straight and apolo-gise unreservedly to Mr Lemmy for any damage done to his reputation.

Wannabes could do to learn from Lemmy. You need to make an effort if you want to survive in showbiz. Do some-thing memorable. Bring props. Some years later I was sent to interview the former fiancée of *Pop Idol*'s Rik Waller. She did her best, reporting that they had romped on the duvet over the remnants of a bucket of KFC. No bondage. No uni-forms. No lesbians. No good. 'With that attitude he'll never last,' muttered Crump, as the story was confined to the back pages.

'How's the car running?' Dad asked the next day.

He didn't mention Lemmy. I'm not sure my parents have

'Snake Bite Love' in their record collection, come to think of it.

Really, the questions you are asked by your parents are an indication of how your life's going. Ideally, by this age, I should really have been answering questions about how my adoring husband was. My parents should have been looking forward to grandchildren. Getting cards signed 'from us' at Christmas, instead of the ones, year after year, signed just from me.

Christmases were to be doomed for the next ten years. I would arrive back home for three days which I would spend in an increasingly foul mood from nicotine withdrawal.

My dad would worriedly stand with his head in my car bonnet shortly after my arrival back home murmuring that he was sure he 'could smell smoke' and start sniffing the dip-stick.

I was spending every Christmas Eve in my old childhood bed in my old childhood bedroom, which still contained its old love-heart wallpaper and matching duvet set and had my Grade 5 ballet certificate on the wall. And I was to pretend my life had stayed that wholesome.

I know I wasn't the only one lying to my parents about how things had changed. I know that because I'd wait until I heard snoring from my parents' room then light up a furtive cigarette in the midst of the night, leaning out from my bedroom window. Across the housing estate, I'd see a series of bedroom windows, all lit with cigarette glows. All moving to the silhouetted heads of the children who had come home for Christmas. We waved to each other across the tarmac of our respectable cul-de-sac as we inhaled our secret smokes as our parents slept. None of us wanting to spoil the magic of Christmas by admitting we'd incurred a forty-a-day habit since we left.

But I was perhaps the only one in the neighbourhood who was calling home trying to avoid the subject of Lemmy from Motörhead.

Instead we talked about the car.

'Did you book it for an MOT?' he asked.

Of course, what he probably really meant was, What the Hell was that in the paper about Lemmy? Do you know how much we spent on your education? You got an A in Physics for goodness' sake. What are you doing?

'Does it still smell of smoke?'

I was, back then, secretly extremely pleased with my first kiss-and-tell and had read it quietly to myself several times and admired the sight of my byline above it, but it wasn't really the sort of milestone you could chat about with your parents. They could hardly put it up on display, next to my old ballet certificates, ready for when I came back next Christmas, could they?

Looking back, it was an awful shame for them. They spent my formative years worrying about what school to send me to, and whether it was okay to let me stay up past 9 pm on weekdays, and was I getting enough vitamins and roughage, and learning my periodic tables. And they'd probably told everyone to look out for my amazing newspaper career. And, after all that work, I'd squandered the lot on Lemmy.

Meanwhile the reports of life back home, the life I should have been leading, and the sort of people I should have been leading it with, continued.

'I bumped into your old English teacher, Mrs V,' my mum said one day. 'She asked how you were getting on.'

Dear Mrs V, who had patiently taught me grammar. Who used to Blu-Tack my poems to the wall at primary school so they were up on display as an example of what could be achieved. She even won me £50 once, by sending off a short story of mine to a writing competition. A fortune when you're twelve years old. I bet she'd get a bit of a shock if she looked at my latest essays.

'I'm fine,' I said. 'Tell Mrs V it's all fine.'

'She wanted to know if you'd maybe come and give a talk to the pupils at the primary school,' Mum said.

Best not, I thought. Even if I had proved I could conjugate the verb 'to whip' correctly, I may not be a shining example of what could be achieved if you always did your homework on time.

So, back home we never mentioned anything about Himmler or helmets. We never mentioned anything about any of the odd things I was to write about over the years. They staunchly and generously told me they were proud of me and my career and each year we watched *EastEnders* on Christmas Day and nothing was said when Dean Gaffney came on screen.

This was all for the best really. After all, I was about to start hiring hookers.

5

MY GIGS WITH GIGOLOS

And the Art of Handling Hookers

Let me walk you through a newspaper office, and my lowly place in it at this time. It will help explain all the prostitutes I was seeing in those days. A year had passed and I'd clung on, turning up each day for shifts. I'd managed a few more bylines on the way. Most of which contained the word 'lust'. No staff jobs had yet come up. I was still facing a grim daily battle to keep my job and I still continued to say 'yes' to absolutely every job that was thrown my way. Unfortunately, saying 'yes' to everything in a newspaper office can lead you to some very odd situations.

National newspapers are huge operations and, on the editorial side, they are divided into sections of reporters. As a shifter you simply go wherever they send you.

There are some nice places to end up in journalism. There

is the Sports section. Here all the reporters are all really quite jolly as they get to go off to the football all day, and get to ask nice interview questions to footballers like, 'Talk me through that brilliant goal you scored, then', rather than ''Ere, what's all this about Ulrika?' Impertinent quizzings like that are the job of the Showbiz desk – a liver-hardened lot who lead a vampirical existence in darkened night-time bars. The upside for them is that they can get the glory of a front-page story without ever leaving the pub, whenever someone really important like Posh gets their hair done.

There is the Royal beat – full of nice toffs in three-piece suits with three-piece names to match. They spend a lot of time checking dress codes on invitations and going to garden parties. I'd sit near them sometimes, and could detect a faint waft of disapproval whenever I shouted over to the newsdesk that my interview with a topless model was almost done. Some months earlier I had worked for one day on the Royal beat and thoroughly enjoyed it, but was quickly thrown off as my northern accent wasn't really deemed posh enough to ring Buckingham Palace and my two-piece name was deemed too common to appear on invitations issued by royal command. 'Please, please,' fluttered one pale man with a retreating chin an hour into my sole day shifting there, 'I entreat you not to answer the phone with your name.'

Being a columnist on the Features desk looked fun, I'd often think. Every paper has one of them. You get paid stacks and get to have a never-ageing photograph of yourself printed in the paper at the top of your column – usually in flattering black and white, and heavily airbrushed so you look thin and wrinkle-free. The actual columnists are all about ten years older than their byline pictures. The first time I saw Julie Burchill, I thought she was her own mother. All you basically have to do on these columns is slag people off all day. You don't have to be at your desk until noon either, and you get full lunch breaks too.

Politics is quite a jolly place. Bars in the House of Commons are subsidised, can be open twenty-four hours a day, and many don't have phone reception so the politics reporters often disappear off there for a few hours of alcohol-fuelled peace and say they are 'working' with 'contacts'. There's not much The Editor can do about it. Plus there are lots of lovely leather benches that you can sleep on if you get a bit tired and emotional and miss your last train home.

Fashion is a nice place to be too – full of lots of lovely thin girls in high heels with bouncy, shiny hair. Everyone is nice to the Fashion girls in the hope they will get some new shoes out of it. I would have liked to have ended up there too. But I didn't.

There's one more place. Right, right back, at the end of the reporters' room, a dimly lit corner under a layer of grime. No one really goes over there. Occasionally, a shadowy shape will scuttle from here at dusk to deposit an expense claim for brothels with the secretary, but that's about it. This is the odd bunch of people known as the Investigations team. This is where I was sent next.

Looking back, I can see that this morning, the morning I was told to go to the shadows of Investigations, was when I really started to mess up my personal life in earnest. There's quite a bit of weird stuff coming up in the next few bits, so apologies if you're of a sensitive nature, but just be glad you're not my parents and bear with me.

I managed to get out of the shadows in the end. But back then, an average day started something like this:

8 am. In Conference. The Editor: Right. I need someone to hire me a male hooker.
8.01 am. At my desk. News Editor: Right, you. I wouldn't bother taking off your coat.

Incidentally, you may think it odd that I was referred to as 'you' at this point. Actually 'you' is quite affectionate for a newsdesk. You can really only expect to be called 'Shifter' for at least the first six months of your life. After that, you're just pretty much known by your surname. 'Crump, come here!' Or by rank, if you've made it up high in the paper, 'The News Ed says The Editor's in a foul mood again.'

If you really mess up or do something really outrageous, you'll be known for ever by a nickname, which can be worse. Brownfinger was one example. And another man, not the sharpest tool in the box, was forever known as Domestos – because The Editor once commented that he was 'thick but directable'. A man called Wollice thought he was secretly dating another reporter. But everyone had found out, and for years afterwards she was always known as Gromit.

Anyway. I was still 'you', which was fine by me as long as they were still employing me, and I was still in with a shot of getting that staff job.

Investigations is not an easy sector. It's hardly surprising that one of their reporters was doing all that screaming and brandishing of firearms during my first day in the office. To get a story in the paper when you're an investigative reporter you have to work hard. Really hard. New hairstyles don't cut it over there. Not even when Spice Girls get them.

As an investigative reporter you've got to tackle international vice rings, confront rampaging hooligans and spend lots of quality time with prostitutes. It's a tough gig and they have to be tough people to survive. Even the hardest of hardmen Donal MacIntyre, who's known for tackling football thugs and facing the most dangerous of situations, only managed it for a couple of years and ended up crying like a baby after getting mugged on TV, eventually running off for a break in the light, the safety and the sequins of *Dancing on Ice*.

Anyway, on this day, on my first day in Investigations, I was to be working with a man who had not yet managed to make his escape, sequinned or otherwise. He was called Robert.

Robert had been an investigations reporter for over thirty-five years, and had developed into a wizened, chain-smoking, bruised and battered old beast as a result. Now pushing sixty, he had decades of pain and vice etched on his brows. His face was weary, weathered and withered and there was nothing it hadn't seen. I noticed he sort of slithered across the carpets towards The Editor's office whenever he was summoned.

Still, Robert was a quick worker, I'll give him that. The Editor's request was on odd one . . . The town of Banbury was to be given government-funded sex education lessons, and The Editor had decided that we were to prove that the town was a hotbed of lust. 'I bet the birds there hire male hookers,' said The Editor. 'Find me a male hooker who'll say he regularly services the lusty ladies of Banbury, and find him now.'

I wouldn't have known where to start but, less than five minutes after the call for the gigolo had been raised, Robert slithered over announcing he had a male prostitute who'd been booked and would be waiting in a Banbury Travelodge by 3 pm. Apparently there are websites where these sort of people can be found at a moment's notice.

Anne raised a float for £700 to cover 'miscellaneous gigolo expenses' and politely handed it all over in a brown envelope. Robert gestured to a BT van, which was waiting in the car park outside, and told me to get in. We set off, planning hooker tactics on the way.

A note on the van. A BT van is the transport of choice for every undercover reporter. You can tell fake ones being driven by journalists from the real thing as they all have mirrored windows in the back. These mirrors are one way – enabling you to sit inside and take photographs without anyone being able to see inside. A BT van can be parked on any street corner, for hours . . . days . . . weeks, without arousing suspicion. In the back is the second crucial piece of kit for an investigative hack – several empty Lucozade bottles. I'll leave it to your imagination to work out what they are for, but suffice it to say, the good undercover hack does not emerge for days from his hiding spot. Not even for a comfort break.

Incidentally, the Lucozade technique is a good one, but only when combined with common sense and decent timing. It was once used by a tipster who hid in a church organ for sixty hours before the christening of Madonna's son Rocco, managing to stay there undiscovered as security and A-listers filed in around him. Sadly, having stayed there for sixty hours, and taken what would have been a highly lucrative video of the top-secret event, the idiot then got overexcited and ran out from his hiding place just minutes after the cathedral guests had left. He was caught by security who were still standing outside the cathedral grounds and our hero ended up in court trying to come up with a reasonable explanation as to why he had been sitting in a church organ for three days with a camera and three, now somewhat soggy, bin liners.

Anyway, today should not be as dramatic; the BT van was merely driving to a hotel, where full sanitary facilities were, happily, to be included, as well as a prostitute. I settled into the front, firmly holding onto my own drink supply (as advised by Crump), and tried not to think about the bottles I could hear rattling about in the back.

'This is how we'll do the story. We are pretending to be husband and wife,' began Robert, lighting the first of the sixty Capstan Full Strength he was to smoke that day. Hang on, I thought. You can't just announce we're married like that. I was starting to feel cheap. For a start, Robert was at least thirty years older than me, a foot shorter, only had four teeth, and was sporting a grubby stone-washed denim jacket and jeans combo. Even if I was pushing a size sixteen in those days, I still like to think I would have turned him down. Even as a fake husband. Or at least would have liked some time to think about it, rather than just having yet another imaginary long-term relationship from the newsroom thrust upon me (although, at least I'd made it up a fake aisle this time . . .).

'Don't worry. He'll believe us,' snarled Robert, with a glance at my thighs which were sticking to his plastic seats. He stifled out my squawks of protest in a cloud of Capstan filth. 'We will pretend to be husband and wife and we'll say we can't have sex any more.' Well, at least the cover story was becoming more plausible, I glowered, wishing the van windows, which were glued shut, would open. 'I'll say I've bought you a prostitute as a thirtieth birthday present to satisfy you.'

'I'm only twenty-seven,' I objected. It was overruled.

'Don't worry. He'll believe us. And I've told him that I'm rich, too,' he added through the fug. 'So you might want to get rid of that jewellery as it's a giveaway you're not.' Cheeky fuck, I thought. Frankly, I'd have thought that arriving in a dodgy van would be more of a giveaway. But he reminded me I was new, and desperate for a staff job, so I removed my genuine cubic zirconia bracelet as instructed.

We pulled into a Travelodge two hours later. Clearly, even though he was a rich man, my husband's largesse did not stretch as far as five-star hotel. If I was going to marry a toothless, chain-smoking hobbit, I sulked, I liked to think that I would at least have insisted on a higher thread-count of bed sheet in the evenings. But my argument was, once again, quashed.

'I'm spending £500 on a hooker for you. That's a decent birthday present,' he said. 'Right. He'll be here in half an hour. Get into the bedroom. Here's the plan.'

The 'plan' was that our male prostitute friend would arrive and Robert, who was now suited, booted, and resplendent in gold jewellery, would greet him. He'd then tell him that 'the wife' was in the hotel room, waiting, and the hired hooker would be sent in. Robert would leave a bag on the table containing a hidden camera, carefully angled to tape the pair of us through a veiled side-vent. I was to ask the hooker about his 'services', and his 'charges', get him to talk about his 'conquests' and the 'ladies of Banbury's needs'. Finally, I would photograph him as a 'souvenir'. Then I was to decide I was 'too shy' and 'loved my husband too much' (steady on) to go through with our encounter, before making my excuses and leaving. Robert would be next door, listening in, and would come in and pay him off once it was, literally, all in the bag. If I had any problems at all, I only had to knock on the wall and he'd come straight in to rescue me.

It all seemed bloody complicated. All this to-ing and fro-ing and wheeling, dealing and lying, just to get a young man to admit that he was having a whale of a time servicing sex-starved ladies for cash. 'Can't we just ring him and ask for a straightforward sit-down chat? He might like the publicity,' I ventured.

'I've been hiring prostitutes for twenty-five years now,' snapped Robert. 'Trust me. They do not "like the publicity". They do not do "straightforward sit-down chats" with news-papers. This is the way tabloids work. If you want to work on one, then just do what I say.'

So I did. And my husband disappeared. Leaving me sitting on the hotel bed, waiting for my prostitute lover. Wondering what on earth my old English teacher Mrs V would have said if she could see me now . . . I guessed she wouldn't want me to give a talk any more.

Half-an-hour later I was banging on the wall furiously. With my fists. A confused and naked prostitute was standing in front of me. Male gigolos move a bit more quickly than I had expected. This one, when he turned up, was actually bloody good looking. He looked like John Travolta circa

Grease, in fact. Seriously. I had been turned down by a lot worse.

I managed a skittish smile as he breezed up in the room with a whitened grin and said, 'Oh, hello. To be honest I'd have probably done you for free.'

I coyly offered coffee. He took his clothes off and offered nookie. Unfortunately at this point I realised he was sitting on the table, where the camera bag had been. The bag and its hidden tape recorder had been moved to the floor, where it was currently filming our ankles. Where, presumably, the prostitute was expecting my knickers to be.

I wasn't quite sure what the etiquette was at this point. Either for interviewing prostitutes, dealing with naked men or adjusting hidden cameras – I was fairly inexperienced with all three. I took a couple of photos and tried to smile in a winsome manner as I asked about Banbury. He was stark naked by this point which was distracting to say the least, as I still had a list of about ten questions to get through regarding past conquests, prices and services. His entreaties for hanky-panky were becoming annoying. On the other hand, I could hardly start getting cross with him over his behaviour. After all, he was simply doing his job. If you hired a cleaner you'd hope she'd be getting out her mop and sponge within five minutes of getting through the door, rather than sitting down for a chat. I suppose he was just being professional.

I thought I may as well start the pre-agreed chat about the local lasses and did so, looking him firmly in the eye, and only occasionally glancing at the bag and wondering how best to retrieve it.

He must have mistaken my downward glance for coyness, rather than panic. 'Is this your first time? Come here,' he said, reassuringly. 'Your husband says he doesn't mind. And I don't mind. So come here.' He took hold of one end of the belt around my waist and pulled. His foot kicked the camera bag back as he did so. It was now filming the ceiling. And possibly part of my stricken face.

'Ah,' I said, stalling. Staring at the bag. The only option for retrieving it, I calculated, was to bend at a fairly awkward angle which would leave me prostrate over the prostitute's knee, in what, I was guessing, may be interpreted as flirtatious behaviour. I tried it anyway.

'Oh,' he said. 'Are we after a spanking, then?'

At this point I decided the best option was blind panic, pulled back upright and banged on the wall. Perhaps if my 'husband' came in, I thought, it may provide a distraction to cover camera rearrangement, and we could continue our discussion on film afterwards.

So I knocked. The room stayed 'husband'-free.

It still contained a prostitute though. Who was still staring at me. 'Come here,' he said. 'Naughty girl,' he added.

I carried on with the blind panic bit. And the knocking. And the saying 'Ah' a lot.

The room was still noticeably lacking in husbands. The hooker sauntered over to me again and began to tug at my belt. His other hand started upwards of my knee. I had a sudden rush of shame as I remembered I had really bad knickers on and holes in my tights. Before remembering that I wasn't actually having sex with him, so it didn't really matter.

'Ah,' I said again. 'Ah,' and I knocked frantically on the wallpaper. No answer. By now the gigolo was getting a bit confused at all the rapping on the wall. 'What are you doing?' he said. Entirely reasonably. 'Is this some sort of Morse code foreplay?'

Being completely unable to think of anything reasonable to tell him back, I just screamed 'Ah!' and ran out the room.

At this point I realised that my 'husband' Robert was not answering my knocks because my 'husband' Robert was not next door.

My 'husband' Robert, it emerged, when I phoned him seconds later, was actually twenty miles away, in the van, half way down the motorway on his way to another job with another prostitute. My 'husband' Robert had, until this point, entirely forgotten that he'd left me, his 'wife', on the previous job with the last one.

I was appreciative of the stress and confusion that multiple prostitute juggling must involve and so kept my argument reasoned: 'Where the fuck are you? What the fuck do you mean you're on the M40? I've got a fucking hooker here. I'm fucking leaving,' I told him, pretty calmly I thought.

'No, you're not. You owe me £500,' said the naked hooker who had also emerged into the corridor at this point. He was also making a reasonable argument. He was, after all, in his place of employment, doing his pre-agreed job, and was entirely right to say he was therefore entitled to his salary.

'Just pay him off. Get rid of him,' said Robert from the outside lane of the M40.

I couldn't, I told him. The brown envelope to cover 'miscellaneous gigolo expenses' was with Robert, in his pocket, and therefore en route to the other hooker. My bag, and purse, were also on their way to her – they were in the back of the van, next to all the Lucozade bottles.

'I've only got a tenner,' I told my husband. And my hooker.

'For fuck's sake,' they replied in unison.

Robert said he'd come back. In two hours. 'Oh for God's sake, why are you flapping so much?' he added. 'You've got a nice hotel room . . . and he seems like a nice man. You'll be okay.'

Okay? I was penniless, car-less, fake husband-less and trapped in the Travelodge with a very confused, out-of-pocket and (indeed, entirely out-of-pockets) prostitute.

'Incidentally, would you please put some clothes on?' I added to the latter.

He shrugged. He wasn't going anywhere or taking any more orders without his cash, he said.

One hundred and twenty minutes of small-talk later, during which I filmed the ceiling, Robert arrived back at the hotel.

'You're weird,' the hooker remarked, shaking his head, as he left the pair of us. 'What do you think you're doing?'

The film, I later realised, was unusable. It consisted of my ankle, my ear, a beige lampshade, some vague remarks about Banbury and a lot of off-screen shouting. I had basically just spent £500 of the paper's money begging a hooker to put his clothes back on, and hadn't even got a line about a Banbury cock-horse out of it. I was rubbish.

Marvellous, I thought as Robert drove us back to London with me in a wordless fury all the way. Here I am at the age of twenty-seven. Single. Shagless. Now unable to keep the attention of a toothless, pensioner fake husband. Couldn't even score with a hired hooker. Things were not going well.

Maybe I should have taken the gigolo up on his offer. I did keep hold of his telephone number for a while and contemplated ringing to see if he was still up for the freebie he'd mentioned, but decided I couldn't face the rejection.

Anyway, he was the only man to offer any bedroom activity for a while. I would like to say I spent this period of my life as an empowered singleton. Someone who embraced her freedom, didn't need a man in her life, was an independent woman who chose to remain that way and didn't want the shackles of a relationship.

This, however, would be complete tosh. In truth, I was getting a bit worried about the whole no-man thing by now. I'd been actively trying to get a bloke and going on dates and things, but it became increasingly obvious that no one actually wanted me as their girlfriend. It wasn't just confused hookers on undercover jobs, all men seemed to recoil in horror.

Worse still, everyone else suddenly seemed to be *in love*. Even the girls in London. My weekends seemed to consist of a series of engagement parties which I'd pretend I was pleased to be attending and, naturally, happy for the happy couple. I was starting to think that I too, would rather like a big party where I could show off a ring and a handsome adoring man who would turn round and tell everyone that I was the nicest woman he'd ever met and he wanted me to be by his side forever. But it never happened. Soon I became the only singleton in my group of friends. The only one without a boyfriend. The only one without a Plus One.

Looking back, my problem was that I refused to believe it was my fault. I was completely In Denial. Being single was not my fault, was it? I wasn't doing anything wrong, was I? Okay, so Tippex Tracy was on her third kid by now, as was everyone else who my parents seemed to meet in Tesco's. And I couldn't even get to a third date. But it wasn't my fault that my ovaries remained unsuccessful, was it? I was just unlucky.

My loved-up girlfriends were unswervingly supportive of me as man after man abandoned me. Every Sunday we would meet for their wine and my whining and they'd dissect who'd rejected me over the previous seven days.

'He's an idiot,' they would say. 'I can't believe he hasn't phoned,' they would say. 'It's not you,' they would say. 'It's him.'

I love my friends. They were loyal, sweet and understanding. They were also lying through their teeth.

It was me.

It seems obvious when I look back, but a life in tabloids wasn't exactly making me marriage material.

Looking back, I cringe when I see what I could have won. It wasn't as if I didn't have my chances. I was still young at the time. In my twenties. I was perfectly reasonable looking, perhaps a little sturdier than average in the thigh department, but nothing to make you wince. The occasional man would stop me in a bar, buy me a drink and take my number. And some of them really could have been Mr Right.

There was a marketing director who looked a little like Erik Estrada from CHiPs (circa his 70s heyday that is, one recent picture I've seen of him suggests he's more Paunch than Ponch these days). I met the Estrada-a-like at the back of a nightclub and he took me for lovely dinners in Belgravia. Now, bearing in mind I was living in a hostel and usually had Pot Noodles, this was heaven. We had three courses, an *amuse bouche*, truffles . . . He wore tailored suits and paid for my taxi home. Oh, I should have kept hold of him. But I was six courses into our relationship when he told me sadly, 'it just wasn't working out'.

There was a policeman who lived in Amersham who had a passing look of Robert de Niro. My parents were very hopeful when they heard about him. But he only lasted one evening before claiming he was 'busy' and would ring when 'work quietened down'. Poor man must have had a ten year rush on at the Met. For he never did call.

And there was the artist. He sketched me in a coffee shop, and handed the picture over with his details and a message saying, 'you'd look so beautiful if you smiled'. A romantic and an artistic step-up from the usual builder's shout of, 'Cheer up love, it might never happen'. He was penniless back then, but charges a fortune for his paintings now. I could have had a mews house in Battersea. Except he left me too. After just one iced bun and coffee date. He said it was a busy time too. Must have been a boom time for portraits in London.

My parents were unfailingly optimistic.

'Never mind,' my mum would say. 'Plenty more fish in the sea.'

The sea was indeed full of fish, but none seemed to want to be netted by me.

The problem I think – and I've looked at several dating books over the years – was definitely my small talk. The books suggest girls talk about their parents on their first date, or their siblings, or needlework, flowers and cats.

I didn't. I talked about what I'd done at work that day. In retrospect, that may have been a mistake. What was fast becoming normal in a newspaper office must have proved a little startling to outsiders.

In all honesty, I can't blame them all. Now I can see where I was going wrong, but at the time I just didn't realise. You get so tough. So hardened to it all. Wife swapping in Blackpool and the Travolta lookalike gigolo were just the start of a long line. Vice dens became part of the day job. Like Mike in Investigations, I'd got bored of them. It had all became a bit tiresome, strapping on a hidden camera, climbing into a rubber dress and scouring fetish clubs, trying to see if there was anyone there from daytime TV. I'd recount tales from these jobs in a monotone, whilst eating, and ended each tale with a nonchalant shrug as I turned to my date and enquired, 'So, anyway, what did you do last night?'

I remember one particular job somewhere in Birmingham – I think I was looking for the local mayor in one particular dungeon – smoking a cigarette to try and stay awake whilst the carnage went on around me.

'Please,' said a passing sadist. 'Please could you not smoke in here? It's dangerous.'

I'd told this tale in the office. It got a hearty laugh. So I repeated it during a date with a bank manager, hoping to impress. It got a less rapturous response. I guess you've got to know your audience. When I think back, he'd mainly tended to centre his conversation on ISAs.

The bad news was that I still had plenty of equally unsuitable jobs for a woman ahead of me. Plenty of things that would frighten off any potential dates and ensure I had a lousy love life for years to come.

Six months further down the line I was still clinging onto the job. The contest of the shifters was down to me and Robohack. Other shifters had come and gone, but only the two of us were hired on a daily basis. There had been a tricky moment when a stunning blonde shifter had arrived, fresh from her award-winning work on a regional paper. But happily she'd just left. The unfortunate lass had made the mistake of accepting a lift from a male reporter the week before. Unfortunately, a drinking session had preceeded this, and, without wanting to broadcast much more of her shame, the young lady found herself prostrate on his passenger seat somewhere off the A4 murmuring, 'Give it to me Daddy' in a lay-by. Unfortunately, by 8 am the next day she was renamed Dashboard by the office in honour of where her ankles had ended up. The Daddy journalist had stopped back at the office on his way home after dropping her off, and sent an office-wide email with full details of his conquest.

Dashboard had entered the office in the morning to a round of applause.

'Game on,' Crump had muttered, pulling in his stomach as she approached. 'Need a lift anywhere?' he had offered.

'Never,' said Anne, who found Dashboard in shame-filled tears in the ladies loos. 'Never get involved with a hack, my dear.' Poor Dashboard only lasted until lunchtime, when she took home the cab she would forever wish she'd taken the night before.

So now, it was me versus Robohack. The end was in sight and on I soldiered. As the shifts continued to come, so did the wages, and I decided it was time to take the plunge beyond the bunk-bed. I decided my professional chances would perhaps be improved if I didn't have to start the day queuing for a communal shower and end it watching toe corn inspections. And my love life might improve away from the bunions. So I moved out of the hostel, away from the noisy ballerina, and into a flat-share in Kilburn.

My parents visited and were relieved that for the first time they didn't have to step over homeless people on their way to my bathroom. Finally I had a bedroom big enough that my parents didn't have to stand in it in shifts when they visited. Finally, things were looking up.

Not really.

Should you ever find yourself flat hunting in London, don't ever go for the first one you find in the back of a newspaper which is roughly in budget and think 'that will do'. Ask questions. The flat was owned by two hippies. I entirely misunderstood them when they said that they both 'smoked and did I mind?' when I came to check out the flat. Turned out they meant they both smoked twenty spliffs a day. Being utterly naive, I hadn't realised what the sweet stench was in the front room and merely thought it was incense. Okay, so I'd spent over a year in vice dens by now, but they're all strictly non-smoking because so many of the guests are flammable. Stupidly I'd decided the flat was roughly in budget and had taken it. It was when my parents came and sniffed the air suspiciously and stared at my horizontal flatmates that I realised what I'd done. Sadly by this point I'd already signed a twelve-month lease.

Over the next year I resigned myself to coming home from whatever Hell had been unleashed on me that day, to sit exhausted with the resident cat in a stoned haze, eating biscuits. I began to miss the bunions.

But, cannabis fug aside, I was finally moving up in the world. I did, after all, have a double bed for the first time in my life. Surely, I would now find a man to fill it I thought, as I lay there on my first night in my new home. My love life was bound to start looking up.

Not really. Oh, I was destined to lie there alone for years yet. My friends bought me a goldfish as a moving-in present, but four weeks later it committed suicide by jumping out of its tank.

You know, those things only have a four second memory and yet still couldn't deal with my life.

I can hardly blame it though. The stuff I was about to see will remain etched in my memory for ever.

6

FAKING MYTHICAL BEASTS

And the Art of Withstanding a Bollocking

A thudding was coming deep from the bunker of The Editor's office, as I slunk to my desk some months later, after yet another uneventful night under my duvet. I was still shifting. Still fighting for that staff job. I'd managed to accost Kate Winslet's fiancé in a pub and get a few lines out of him about their upcoming wedding and being in love, and uncovered a line that Samantha Fox was rumoured to be a lesbian, which had caused a flurry of excitement and a few days hanging hopefully around on doorsteps. A few women had slagged off Darren Day for being a love rat, but that was about it. No splashes. Nothing that was going to win me a Pulitzer if I'm honest.

Robohack was doing much better. He'd invested in a white coat and spent a day wandering around a hospital unchecked, pretending to be a doctor, until he finally found a celebrity who we'd heard had just been wheeled into intensive care. The resultant picture of the celeb, with tubes and wires trailing from their mouth and heart had run under a 'World Exclusive' headline and Robohack was now being hailed as a star by The Editor.

Okay, so it hadn't exactly been an approved photo call. 'But he never objected to his picture being taken,' smirked Robohack, as he arrived back with the film. The celeb in question had been in a coma at the time.

A yelp came from The Editor's office as I leafed through the me-free newspaper. It sounded like a wild animal was thrashing about inside the blacked-out doors. After a minute and a dozen thuds, Crump flew out, fell to his desk and sucked desperately at his asthma inhaler.

'Now that,' he wheezed, 'was a *major* bollocking.'

At this point in my life, several people asked me why on earth I was bothering to go back to work each day. After tax, a shifter gets around £70 a day, the hours were lousy and the job description not exactly idyllic.

But it's the high of getting a story into print that more than makes up for this. The papers are delivered to the office, fresh off the press, the night before they reach the newsstands. They arrive wrapped in cellophane, and we leap on them as they arrive, tearing off the covers to get to them. The thrill of seeing your name emblazoned across a paper, under the word 'Exclusive' is a great feeling. It's addictive.

Okay, there was a lot of time spent getting shouted at by strangers. But I'd also had a few scoops and that's what kept me going. It's the word 'Exclusive' that makes it all worthwhile. The thrill of the chase, the joy when you stand up a story, the feeling when you rip open the plastic casing to see your words in print. That's why you carry on. It feels even better when you know every other hack in Britain will be cursing your success and wishing they'd got your story. On the days when you get the front-page splash, you sail out of the office and into the pub on a cloud of smugness. I'd go and stand in newspaper shops the next day, just to look at my story on the stands, just to watch as people leaned over, grabbed it, and started reading my words.

'I wrote that!' I wanted to tell them. I wanted to point at my name as they read the paper. 'That's me!'

Knowing that over four million people could be reading your words that day is why you do it. It's a brilliant feeling of power, of being right at the epicentre of gossip. You knew that story before four million people did – because you chased it, you got it, you made it happen, you wrote it. And it's all right there, under *your* name.

Unfortunately, that feeling accounts for just a tiny, tiny proportion of your working life as a tabloid hack. And all the bits leading up to this are slightly less brilliant. Especially the bits when you're getting a bollocking.

Now, newsrooms are not known for their political correctness. Screaming, swearing and shouting of obscenities across the newsroom is the norm. In fairness, the pressure on The Editor and the paper's bosses – making hundreds of decisions a day and juggling hundreds of stories – is immense. It probably wasn't helped when I had days where my sole contribution to the paper was filming a rentboy's ankle.

Getting yelled at by The Editor is part of the tabloid hack's job. If you're not that keen on being shouted at and not sure that you'd enjoy being branded a 'tosspot' in front of your colleagues, then tabloid papers are perhaps not the place and the career choice for you.

If there had been a particularly big cock-up, say an accidentally slaughtered donkey, or a 'World Exclusive' splashed all over the pages of a rival paper that we'd known nothing about, we knew someone was going to be in for the dreaded visit to The Editor's bunker. There would be a tense silence in the newsroom in the morning, a sense of impending doom as we waited for The Editor to arrive and for the inevitable explosion. Two minutes was usually the limit, before some hack would be called into the inner lair, where the tinted windows muted the fury, until the reporter finally emerged, gasping for air.

These bollockings were the stuff of legend. One reporter came out claiming The Editor had started kicking a football at his head whilst he shouted. During another bollocking, The Editor had worked himself into such a fury that he had burst out of his bunker, running around the office like a demented dog, and screaming at us all, repeatedly slamming his hand onto nearby piles of newspapers to punctuate every syllable. He had ended, dramatically, by swiping the two-foot-high pile of papers on the News Editor's desk to the floor and then storming theatrically back into his room. Half an hour later he took Conference, where it was reported in whispers that he was, 'still white with anger and sort of growling at us all'.

Later that day, The Editor had been secretly taken to Casualty. He'd broken his hand during the earlier rant and had had to sit, white with pain and faint, with the distorted fingers hidden under his desk, trying to work out if he'd lose face by admitting that he needed urgent medical attention.

Of course, we all secretly delighted in his agony. The room was bathed in broad smiles the next day when he came in with his hand in a cast. Although of course, to his face, we all pretended not to have noticed.

When terrified rookies headed off towards the bunker with glassy eyes and coldly sweating foreheads, old timers would hand down survival tips.

'You want to run and position yourself as close to the window as you can, before he can even start shouting,' Brownfinger had advised a condemned shifter one day. 'Get there early and stand in front of the glass. That way there's a good chance that he won't kick the football at your head.'

Domestos had emerged one day from the bollocking box with a jubilant thumbs up to the newsroom.

'I've cracked it,' he said. 'I know how to get through them.'

A group had eagerly followed him out the room to an emergency meeting in the smoking room, where he triumphantly passed on his Holy Grail of survival tips. 'Hold onto the back of the chair and dig your nails into your palms,' he said. 'It really worked. I didn't faint!'

A top psychologist was once called into the office to analyse something or other about body language on *Big Brother*, and watched in amazement as a hack was summoned, by a stream of expletives, into The Editor's office.

'What's going on?' asked the psychologist, when a thudding started beyond the blackened glass. We told him our various tales of woe. Turning pale, he ushered us out into the smoking room and gave emergency coaching tips for survival. A brilliant way to confuse the enemy, apparently, is to stare hard at them – not in the eyes, but at the top of their nose, right between the eyes.

'That prevents them from being able to focus on your eyes, it unnerves and confuses them, without them realising what you are doing,' said the psychologist, making us practise it on him as we inhaled our smokes. 'Try it. I beg you. Good God, the man's a monster.'

All these tips worked. But really, the best thing to do, most said, was shut up and take it. 'You've just got to let him blow the gasket,' said Crump, who spoke from experience. 'It's like a hurricane. It'll pass eventually.'

There were things that made The Editor cross – being late, not ironing your shirt, being drunk in the mornings, taking mind altering drugs in the office – but these usually got a swift ticking off, with no fear of physical violence.

There were things that made The Editor *very* cross. Writs arriving, for example, that usually pissed him off. There was one particularly fierce set of lawyers called Peter Carter Ruck, who used to fax through their legal letters. After particularly dodgy stories were printed, you'd enter the office the morning after to find its author standing by the fax machines on tenterhooks, watching to see if anything was coming through. A beeping of the machine, and the arrival of a piece of paper with the Peter Carter Ruck letterhead was heralded with a moan of, 'Oh no! It's a Peter Carter Fuck!' The office would gather round as the letter, usually containing words like 'libel' and 'malicious, false and defamatory' was read out. You'd know you'd be in for a private meeting with The Editor, which may possibly contain a raised voice and the word 'tosser'. But still. Nothing was likely to be broken.

Rampant stupidity. That was usually a cue for a bit of shouting too. There's an annual award ceremony for journalists known as The Shaftas, in which the most stupid stories that have made it into print each year are read out. BUBBLES THE CHIMP TO TESTIFY IN MICHAEL JACKSON TRIAL (no, he didn't); PAUL DANIELS CHOSEN AS NEXT DR WHO (no, he wasn't); BRITNEY SPEARS TO ADOPT TWO CHINESE CHILDREN (no, she's not); PATSY KENSIT ATE HER HORSE (Er. No. But thank you, the *Daily Star Sunday*).

Getting a Shafta was usually a cue for a bit of a strop. As was any dead animal that we were responsible for. But again, it was all survivable. Pretty low on the bollocking Richter scale. These sort of things happen to a tabloid hack.

No, what really, *really*, hacked off the boss, what really, *really*, led to a full hand-breaking, football-coming-at-your-head, hold-on-to-your-chair-and-dig-in-your-nails-so-you-don't-faint, off-the-scale bollocking, was if the journalist had been caught out trying to con The Editor.

And this was what Crump had just done.

In his defence, he'd been in dire straits at the time. He was a broken man. He'd just spent the entire week trying to interview a mythical creature.

Crump told us the tale in the pub.

'Crump? Find me the Beast of Bodmin Moor,' The Editor had told him, on Tuesday.

Now, tracking down Beasts on Moors is, even at the best of times, a tricky task. But this one was made harder because people, professional people who get paid to look for these kinds of things, had been looking for the Beast of Bodmin Moor for twenty years. And no one had managed to find it.

If you look up the 'Beast of Bodmin Moor' in the history books, you will find that an official Ministry of Agriculture, Fisheries and Food investigation in 1995 – and these chaps are really pretty efficient at these kind of things – had concluded that there was 'no verifiable evidence' of the creature's existence. And they weren't the only ones to have looked.

In fact, if you Google it, it comes up under the category of 'phantom wild cat'. 'Phantom' because pretty much every expert that had ever been consulted had concluded it didn't actually exist. Occasionally, livestock had been found slaughtered on the moors of Cornwall, and the odd villager had reported a ghostly sighting of a shadowy shape in the background, but nothing had ever been photographed, proved, or captured. The general conclusion was that this was one elusive beast. So elusive in fact, that it simply didn't exist.

It was but a myth. A legend. A ghost. It was made up.

'I want it found and photographed by Friday,' The Editor said.

People may imagine a great deal of planning goes into deciding who goes into a paper and what gets printed about them.

Not necessarily. A lot of the time it's just The Editor coming up with 'a great idea' that he wants delivered, and delivered quickly, no matter how improbably impossible it is.

'Find me a mythical beast,' is not that unusual a command, really. Honestly I was lucky not to get a similar one over the years. Although I did get my fair share of odd requests.

I once got forty minutes notice to make it to a flight to Istanbul after a vague hunch from the Royal desk that Prince Harry, 'may have booked a belly dancer for a party' in a restaurant, 'somewhere in Turkey'. I'd been told airily by the News Editor that the town they *thought* Harry was in was just 'a short drive' from the airport, so off I went 'on this little jolly'.

I travelled alone, and as I landed at midday and asked for a local map showing the route to the town, a horrified car rental operative refused to lend me a car. The 'short drive' was actually a 750 kilometre, twelve-hour drive into the night, taking me round the hairpin bends of the unlit mountains, along a route notorious for bandits and hijacking. 'No,' he said, tapping at his head with a finger. 'You crazy, crazy woman. You'll die. You can't do it in a Ford Fiesta.'

In the end, after pleading that my job was at stake and it was a matter of national importance and after emptying my bank account for cash bribes, he got a taxi driver to take me; a taxi driver who insisted on driving a 4×4 and being accompanied by two soldiers from the local barracks for protection. Flanked by the armed protectors, the taxi driver and an interpreter I had to find on the way, we hurtled through the mountains and reached the village at 1 am, where we started door-to-door enquiries.

The poor belly-dancing girl was roused from her bed and slightly bewildered to be met by two members of the armed forces and an exhausted-looking woman in a suit banging on her door in the middle of the night. She had no idea that the men she'd given an eight minute dance to at a restaurant the night before were royal. Or quite what this mad woman was doing, on her doorstep, throwing money at her, asking if she'd pose in her veils, tearfully asking if she could remember anything . . . *any detail at all* . . . about a young boy with red hair.

'Yeah, well done,' said the Night News Editor when I rang at 2 am to say it was in the bag and I was about to start the twelve-hour drive back. 'Took you long enough. Bet you've been pissing about on the beach drinking cocktails and enjoying your little holiday, haven't you? Be at the office first thing.'

Still, at least I came back alive and well from that one. I needed a trip to the doctors and a week bathing in calamine lotion after a day spent lying around a Spanish pool, trying to stand up a rumour that Stan Collymore had gone on holiday with a 'mystery woman'. I was verging on third-degree burns after six hours on my sun-lounger (with a camera under my towel) by the time his villa door finally opened, and out he came with his mother.

Anyway. Today it was Crump's turn to take on a Mission Impossible. Crump was in disgrace at the time. He'd completely missed the story about Danniella Westbrook's descent into massive drug abuse, despite being regular drinking pals with her. 'I didn't think she had a *problem*,' he had wailed to The Editor when the rival paper fell with the story

114

on the front. 'I mean . . . yes, we did cane it a bit the other night, but, hey . . . I just thought she'd had a bad day.'

As punishment Crump was put on Stunt Duty. Stunt Duty is the worst job to get on a paper. Basically, it is the art of being photographed and humiliated for the paper. When David Blaine was in town, hanging in a plastic box somewhere near Tower Bridge and claiming he wasn't going to eat or drink for forty-four days, one reporter also had to sleep and eat in a giant Perspex box – in the middle of the office. To report 'what it was like'. He had CCTV cameras trained on him to check he didn't move and there was a serious discussion at the time over whether he too shouldn't be allowed to eat for forty-four days, to 'ensure journalistic accuracy'.

Another spent a week living in an airing cupboard under the stairs the week Harry Potter launched.

Anyway, today was an easy one in comparison. All Crump had to do on his Stunt Duty was to wear a Sherlock Holmes outfit and catch a ghost.

Crump drank deeply in the pub as we gathered round him for support and he explained what happened next. The instructions from on high were quite loose, apparently. 'Dig some sort of hole and then maybe hide in it until the monster comes,' the newsdesk had suggested vaguely on the Tuesday.

'They gave me a shovel,' said Crump. 'They were genuinely convinced that a mass-murdering demon dog was going to appear in the middle of the night, and all they gave me was a fancy dress outfit and a shovel.'

I bought him another pint and he continued his tale of woe. The problem with the Moor apparently, is that it is about two hundred kilometres square and made entirely of solid granite. Crump and the photographer had arrived, hacked at it with a shovel for a bit, and then generally concluded it was all a bit doomed.

'I told the News Editor it was impossible,' Crump said. 'He said that was "defeatist talk". Nothing is impossible on newspapers.'

Another plan had been hatched on high for our Sherlock. He should set a trap. 'Put out some raw meat to tempt the beast in,' was the helpful suggestion.

So Crump had sat in his car on the Moors, in his Sherlock outfit, together with a moonlit lamb shank.

'I sat there for eight hours,' he lamented over the whisky chaser I brought over.

No mythical beasts arrived from the depths of the Moor to greet our Sherlock or his lamb supper. The next day came the suggestion to perhaps 'try fresher flesh'. At the desk's behest, a live sheep was tethered to his wheel for two hours until a suspicious local, alerted by the bleating, approached the unlikely threesome. You can see why, when confronted with a dishevelled Sherlock, a tethered beast and a cameraman with a long lens, this local chap informed Crump and co. that he was about to report them all to the police for what was clearly some sort of sordid sexual behaviour.

'Apparently it's illegal to tether a sheep. Went mental, he did,' moaned Crump over his third pint. 'How the fuck am I supposed to know what sheep rights are? And what do they mean, you can't tether them? What was I supposed to do with the sheep anyway? Put it in the back seat of the car?'

We shook our heads. God, I'd had it easy with the belly dancer. Marauding bandits and lethal mountain roads pale into comparison to a night spent demon-chasing and trying to get your head around sheep law.

More instructions came from on high. Goat tethering is, apparently, perfectly legal confirmed the paper's legal department, so Crump and the snapper spent another night on the Moor, with a legal goat tied to the wheel.

No phantom beasts arrived.

'I rang the desk at midnight, begging to be let off, but their only suggestion was to maybe put the sheep back. They reckoned it was better at bleating and would perhaps attract more attention,' said Crump. 'Or try a chicken.

'Forty years of age and a private education and they want me to start recreating bloody *Animal Farm* in the back of the car,' Crump sighed. 'I was a broken man. A broken man, I tell you.'

Should you ever find yourself in the situation where a demonic dog is refusing to attend a photo call, here's what not to do.

Don't drive to your nearest zoo, bribe a zookeeper and take a blurry picture of a puma. And certainly don't drive back to the office and announce to everyone that you've cracked it. Definitely do not, *ever*, continue to keep lying through your teeth and allow announcements to go out to the government, and be filmed for a massive TV ad campaign proclaiming yourself a hero, and sit back and watch as five triumphant pages and a splash are laid out claiming you're about to enter the history books.

'The Editor,' said Crump, signalling to the barman to just leave the whisky bottle by his side, 'went *nuts* when he found out the truth.'

7

MY BOOZE SHAME

And the Art of Having a Large One

The News Editor picked his way through the newsroom. The office melted to a halt and stared. Watches were checked. A Sub-Editor murmured, 'It's a new record,' made a note in an A4 pad and high fived him as he passed.

'Conference in ten minutes please,' said the News Editor as he swooped to a ringing phone. 'Newsdesk?' he said. 'Dean Gaffney? Right love. How many people were involved?'

'He's not even slurring,' murmured Anne from beneath a pile of letters marked 'writs', which she was just handing to a worried-looking Robert – my 'husband' – from Investigations. She shook her head in admiration.

I checked my watch. It was 4 pm.

'What's the big deal?' I asked. 'That's not exactly a long lunch. What time did he leave?'

'11 am,' said Anne.

'Oh, okay,' I said. 'Yeah, a five hour lunch *is* fairly impressive.'

'No,' said Anne. 'Eleven o'clock *yesterday* morning.'

I feel it's time to raise the subject of alcoholic refreshment. Actually, I probably should have done it sooner. We never exactly hung about when it came to getting the drinks in when I was a journalist. Anyway, explaining the culture of alcohol will explain a lot about what went on in newsrooms.

Should you still be considering a career in tabloid journalism, even after reading this far, one of the most important things to consider when assessing whether you are cut out to do it is not necessarily your ability to find stories. Or to write them. Or to ask outrageous questions whilst making them appear perfectly normal. No. It is your ability to drink.

Journalists drink. They drink a lot. I drank an awful lot when I was a journalist. And we had an awful lot of fun doing it.

In the original Fleet Street, before the days of mobile phones, the local pubs had phone exchanges which linked direct to the newsdesk. After around 2 pm News Editors would just ring the pub directly and ask to be put through to their staff.

Drinking, I had realised, was fully expected and not frowned on by management. And I had spent the past three years fully embracing this perk of the job. In fact, one senior exec was notorious for arriving at the morning Conferences clutching a bottle of red. I once arrived in the ladies loos at lunchtime to find him face down on the floor in a state of undress, his head hanging half way out a cubicle. I managed to persuade him to zip himself up, then snuck him through the back doors, back to his office, where I propped him back safely in his executive chair and carefully swung it away from the glass door entrance, so it wasn't immediately obvious to passers-by that our leader was completely steaming. He was very grateful. I got a pay rise the following week.

The old hacks, the ones who had been in the business for decades, could file the most beautiful copy whilst blind drunk. One old timer once downed thirty-two pints of Guinness and then returned to his desk, where he wrote a faultless think piece. Knowing him, it was probably on the perils of binge drinking in broken Britain. Drink did fuel creativity. Hacks would emerge from pub sessions with Big Ideas for stories, or just stupid ideas to pass the time.

After one particularly splendid lunch, we decided it would be really funny to make Domestos and Brownfinger take sleeping pills and then have a competition to see who could stay awake the longest. Another day the entire male staff decided to take a Viagra pill just before popping into afternoon Conference. A drunken bet to see who could be most creative on 'National Take Your Pet to Work Day' resulted in me borrowing four meerkats from a local zoo . . . I felt sure I had victory in the bag, until the newsroom doors burst open and the features editor entered, unsteady on his feet but smiling triumphantly as he paraded a lion cub on a piece of string. Another lost day involved a post-lunch bet involving the newspaper's solicitor, who was sure he could ski down a slope, backwards and with one hand tied behind his back, faster than a reporter could going forward. A round-trip to the French Alps was hastily arranged and the two hared off to the airport, caught an EasyJet flight, spent just fifteen minutes on the slopes and then raced back to the office; the lawyer returned in time to deal with any outstanding legal enquiries and confirmed he had indeed proved victorious on the slopes.

Relay Drinking was quite a popular game for a while. There was a pub thirty feet from the main entrance to the newspaper offices, at the top of a hill. The rules stipulated that you had to run from your desk, down six flights of stairs, race up the road, down a pint in the pub and then race back down the road, up the stairs and back to your desk. Your time was recorded with a stopwatch. It started off as a game of News reporters versus Features reporters. In time it became an empire-wide competition, with relay teams from rival newspapers racing up and down the road downing speed pints, as supporting journalists yelled encouragement through the windows.

This was all at about 9.30 am in the morning.

After lunch it got even worse. There is a long-standing rivalry between broadsheets and tabloids, with each convinced they are the 'proper' journalists who print the 'proper' news and have the most influence. Drink fuelled this competitive spirit. The unfortunate hacks from *The Times* have glass-walled offices which face out onto a main road. After one particularly long liquid lunch, our tabloid news team took a detour back from the office and mooned through their windows. God knows what the poor hacks inside thought, as a long line of tabloid reporters' bottoms appeared in the glass. Still, we think we got our point across.

Of course, amidst all this drinking, we still had a paper to get out. I used to write reams of copy completely rat-arsed. We once lost out on serialising a book about Kylie, as a rival paper outbid us for the rights. Not to be outdone, The Editor simply ordered me to write another one. Overnight. I duly did. Twenty thousand words fuelled by two bottles of Merlot. I was as interested as anyone else when it started being serialised in the paper the next day. I hadn't a clue what I'd actually written.

Journalists have a capacity to snap to attention, to type and file, even after the most copious amounts of alcohol. The night of Princess Diana's death, journalists were corralled from distant bars and produced the finest, most beautiful copy in minutes. The old boys, the men in their sixties who'd been doing the job for decades, would go into a sort of trance, fingers blurring across the keyboard as they bashed out reams of faultless copy. You could call them back from pub sessions late at night and ask them to bang out a thousand words and they'd do in minutes what the young journalists would take hours to achieve sober. I loved these men. They're a dying breed and most have been axed now, but back then they were rows of wizened old boys in suits. All with nicotine-stained fingers and moustaches. They had an encyclopaedic knowledge of every piece of gossip on every public figure, reaching back decades. Employed in the years before Google and databases, they had all their facts stored up, coiled and waiting in their heads, ready to be unleashed on a keyboard in emergencies. Years of practice meant they'd click onto automatic and deliver the goods at any time of day or night. It was only when you looked them in the eyes you realised they were absolutely blotto.

Looking back at my old leaving card, it appears my capacity for wine was, even in this environment, seen as quite remarkable. There are several references to red wine. I was known as The Queen Hic.

But lack of sobriety was not a sackable offence. The bosses pretty much turned a blind eye. Although they did, occasionally, get their revenge. One female journalist got a drink-driving ban and feared she'd get an instant dismissal from the paper if she was ever found out. She spent a year with a personal chauffeur on standby, ready to ferry her to any job. After she regained her licence a year later, she threw a party to celebrate. The Editor turned up mid-way through the night and confessed he'd known about the ban all along and had taken great delight in working out each day which job would require the most travel and then sending her to cover it, knowing she would face a fortune in chauffeur's fees.

But everyone drank. Everyone was drunk at some stage in the office. My career was kick-started with booze and it carried on that way for the ten years I worked on the tabloids. It was expected, and, in times of need when you'd overdone it, your colleagues would rally round to help. We had a small glass box-room – about four-foot square – next to the news-desk, with soundproofed walls. It contained an armchair and a TV. If someone was so supremely drunk they could no longer be relied on to stay conscious at their desk, or ran the risk of disrobing and hurling obscenities at The Editor at a moment's notice, we'd throw them into the chair, stick on a DVD of some footage from an undercover job and lock the door. To anyone important, looking in from the outside, it looked like the hack was hunched down and engrossed in watching a tape of 'evidence'. In reality, it bought you at least two hours to sleep things off. I spent a good many afternoons in there. And a few hungover mornings, when an hour's kip during Conference seemed the only way through the day ahead. Sometimes, after big nights like the Baftas, the Press Awards or the Brits – where the bars had been free – the entire newsroom would all be in such a state that we'd all have to take our turns in the box in shifts.

This was all before lunch. In the evenings it got even worse. Crump once went for a 'quick pint' with Sean Ryder and ended up in Ibiza, starring in a documentary about Brits Behaving Badly abroad, being interviewed on Radio One and featuring across a two-page spread in *Loaded*. 'That Sean's a good lad,' he smiled, as he limped back in the next day, still in the same clothes but now lightly sunburned. He'd had a tattoo spelling 'Exstacy' etched into his biceps. For years afterwards the Subs would come and correct it with a felt-tip pen every time he wore a short-sleeved shirt to the office.

That's the fun thing with journalism. Go with the booze-laden flow and you can end up in the oddest and most exciting places, and uncover the most unlikely stories. I once spent a whole day standing on doorsteps looking for the former Prime Minister's son, James Major, to talk about his romance with the glamour model Emma Noble. I gave up at midnight, only to stumble into a nightclub VIP room and find them snogging furiously in the corner. Another hack literally fell over Nicky Clarke on a pavement in St Lucia once after a night out. Nicky was horizontal at the time and snogging a blonde who was not his girlfriend. The hack simply took a quick pic on his camera phone, happy in the knowledge that his entire Caribbean holiday could now go on expenses. Not all nights out could be reported. One political hack once got exceptionally pissed at a boozy Westminster private party. Realising his last train home had long gone, he wandered the corridors of the building that had provided the historic setting for the sophisticated evening, until he chanced upon a room with a lovely four poster bed. Tired and emotional, he snuggled down in the inviting sheets and fell asleep. He wasn't aware of the magnitude of his resting place until, awakened the next day by his ringing phone, he noticed a memorial plaque informing him that the bedroom was the one in which English kings and queens spent the night before their Coronation. The plaque swore blind the bed hadn't been slept in since 1953. Actually, hate to break it to Prince Charles, but by the time he comes to sleep there, the glorious ancestral history of the sheets will have been tainted slightly, by one drunk Commons hack who'd crept in wearing just a pair of underpants and a tired smile.

It wasn't entirely unusual to come in first thing and find reporters in their underpants. If a lock-in had occurred nearby, some would forget about going home altogether and crawl to the office to ensure they were in place come Conference time. The Editor's office had a long leather couch which was a favourite resting place for drunk hacks. The air would often be abuzz of a morning with the sound of dishevelled male hacks dragging electric shavers across their chins at their desks, as they tried to look like they'd made it home. I wasn't any better. Okay, I never actually started shaving in public, but I did spend a couple of nights on that leather couch. And I did keep outfits in the desk drawer, together with fresh knickers, make-up remover, spare shoes and a toothbrush for those mornings when I was still wearing last night's clothes. There's another message in the leaving card: 'When are you going to come and take all these bloody shoes and clothes home?'

Lunch breaks have now been shortened and the in-house bars have all closed down, but still, there really is no place in tabloid journalism for a teetotaller. The pub is the place where mischief was caused and trouble was plotted. The pub is a sanctuary too. The place where grievances could be aired and sorted. Where tales of other people completely cocking-up a job would be shared to make you feel better. Even The Editor used to come to the pub. If he'd just spent the morning kicking a football at your head, calling you a tosser and ordering you about, then he would spend the night ordering you a pint and you would call it quits.

It may not have looked like it to a casual observer, but actually, all these drunk journalists were working. Learning how to hold your booze is an essential skill which can only be honed by years of training. A stone-cold-sober contact will sit in stone-cold-sober silence if interviewed first thing in the morning. Take them out to lunch, get them riotously drunk and then make them carry on drinking into oblivion, and the contact will become an information-spilling wreck by the early hours. Again, the trick is to never look remotely interested in anything they are saying. And then to excuse yourself every half hour to nip to the loo and write the whole lot down on a beer mat, before returning with another round of shots. This beer mat skill is essential, as neither of you will actually remember a word that was said by the morning. The beer mat is often your only clue. There was to be many a morning when I arrived in the office and had to dig around the beer-stained debris of my handbag in the hope of finding a page lead.

The drinking training schedule is harsh. A 9 am whisky 'livener' in the pub, as the bosses depart for Conference, was not unusual. Followed by a bottle of wine at lunch. Followed by another during a long afternoon session with 'contacts', slipping casually into an evening's absolute bender.

I drank a lot of the old falling-down juice as a hack. Back at the age of sixteen, on work experience on my local paper, I would be paid, per story, with a Brandy and Babysham at the local pub, by a News Editor who I remember had the admirable skill of being able to down a pint of Claret in 3.8 seconds. And I never stopped. Some days, some weeks and, to be honest, pretty much all of my late twenties are a bit hazy. I had to look back through the newspaper to remember where I'd been that week. They greeted me in Oddbins like family.

I suspect the physical effect on our bodies was probably not that brilliant. You can spot the newest recruits in jour-nalism. They look sort of shiny, new, thin and clean. After a few years we all looked a bit fuzzy round the edges and had gone a bit grey. Crump's poor body was so dehydrated that once, when he was on Stunt Duty (again), he was sent to test out a colonic irrigation system for a feature. The bewildered nurse sent four pints of warm water shooting up him to no effect. 'They reckon my body just absorbed the lot,' he had shrugged when he returned to the office two hours later, still waterlogged.

But still, on we drank. Because drinking was fun. And drinking was funny. And it just helped you forget about all the bad stuff. Like the fact that by now I was officially, statistically, proven to be undatable.

I know this because I did something bad. Something desperate, lonely and shocking. Something shameful. Something that still makes me shudder when I think how low I stooped. Something I definitely didn't tell my parents about.

I went speed dating.

I'd hit thirty by now. So I was starting to worry about the still being single thing. Thirty is quite a big life milestone. It sounds quite grown-up. Yet my life hadn't done any growing up at this stage. I hadn't achieved anything which looked remotely adult. So, general-panic-about-being-thirty. That's my excuse. Because speed dating's a bit shameful, a bit furtive. It is a club for losers, isn't it? For people who cannot pull by ordinary means. By signing up, I was admitting that the only way I could be expected to get a life partner was to go to a special room; a room which was filled solely with other losers like me, who had also been dumped into the dating category marked 'failure'. Between us, we members of this community of rejects, were to sift through the debris of life's dating runts, in the hope that somewhere there would be someone that would take pity on us and take us home.

Of course, they don't quite put it like that in the adverts.

They're all a bit more upbeat about the whole thing. The one I found on the internet promised it was a, 'Fantastic way to meet new people and have a great night out'.

But let's be honest. Speed dating's not a great night out, is it? No. It's shit.

Think about it. Think about all the bright, successful, celebrity women that I was writing about in the paper. They didn't have to go speed dating, did they? You would never, ever, find Keira Knightley sitting in a room in a pub, with a name badge on, hoping someone would give her a 'yes' tick so she'd get to see them again. Madonna? She'd never pay cash to sit in a room being told what to do by a 'Speed Dating Leader' and receiving email assurances that the entrance fee she'd just paid over the internet would, 'guarantee at least ten exciting dates tonight!'.

No. They all just meet people and fall in love. Like normal people do. It was just losers like me who needed to shell out hard cash in order to get the opposite sex to talk to them.

Anyway. Off I went. 'Oh, that'll be a laugh,' said my friends. My married friends.

Of course speed dating is not a laugh. Speed dating is grimly serious. It is the last-chance saloon for the undatable and there was an air of tension in the room which hit me from the moment I arrived at the pub door, saw the sign announcing 'Speed Dater This Way!' and followed its arrow to the back of the pub, where the unlovable masses had gathered together in the gloom.

The arrow directed me past all the bright, happy, paired-off normal people at the bar. Back towards the pack of losers where I belonged. Where a group sat in silence, nervously scanning each incoming face and staring intently at the pieces of paper which had been carefully placed in front of them.

'Hello!' shouted a man wearing a 'Speed Dating' T-shirt, emblazoned with a plastic label marked, '*Speed Dating Leader Tony!*' in cheerful red letters. It was like those name-tags supermarket workers wear – 'Happy to help you get laid!' it should have read underneath. He waved at me. I waved back, and shuffled over. *Speed Dating Leader Tony!* asked my name and handed over a little badge with my name neatly written in felt tip under the word 'Speed Dater!'

I put it on. My little red badge of failure.

Speed Dating Leader Tony! smiled and jumped about, handing out pens and badges. After a while, he rang a bell to get our attention, and we – and all the normal people who were staring at us from the normal end of the pub – put down our glasses to listen. He explained he too had once been just like us and gone to a speed dating session, so we had 'nothing to feel embarrassed about'. He was brisk, businesslike and matter of fact. Like an STD nurse assuring you she's seen it all before. I sat, burning with shame.

'In fact,' said *Speed Dating Leader Tony!*, giving us all a cheerful two thumb salute, 'I came to a Speed Dating event and loved it so much I joined the company. Ha ha! Now, we are *unique* in that we guarantee that you will meet someone you would like to see again at one of our Speed Dating events. We're so confident, in fact, that if you don't, your next event is free! Now. Let the outrageous flirting begin!'

He ended on a crescendo. I stayed seated and mute. Outrageous flirting? I looked around nervously. People with badges pinned to their lapels were shiftily moving towards numbered tables.

'You,' said *Speed Dating Leader Tony!*, sweeping over to me, 'are on table five.' He gave me a double thumb salute again.

I found table five, which was laid out with two chairs and two pens. And a piece of paper on either side with four blank boxes. One read 'name' and then there was 'yes!', 'no!' and 'I'd like to see you as a friend' by the side.

A man approached my desk. His badge read, 'Speed Dater Nick!'. 'Nick,' I wrote carefully on my form.

'I've hand-reared five pigs and I'm going to slaughter and eat them,' was Nick's opening gambit. To be honest, I'd been veering towards the 'no' box on first sight. He wasn't a looker. He looked a little like Stephen Merchant from *The Office*, except his eyes were sort of rounder and his head was sort of longer. And he was taller and thinner. He was a most unfortunately shaped young man.

But beggars could not be choosers, and the only husbands and boyfriends in my life were fake ones borrowed from newspaper desks for the afternoon. So I'd smiled and asked him, 'what his hobbies were'. That was what prompted the answer about porcine genocide.

I remembered my journalism training, tried not to look surprised, and left a silence to see if he'd say anything more. He did. 'Apparently, if you feed them lots of beer in their food whilst they're still alive, then you'll really be able to taste beer in the crackling when you eat them,' he added. I left another silence. 'You can send the dead pig off in the post and there's this firm that cuts it all up and then sends it all back in bits. You can specify if you want sausages or bacon. It's brilliant.'

I wrote, 'Sausages. Or bacon' on the notes bit at the side of the paper, gave an encouraging nod, showed him I'd written it all down and signalled for him to carry on.

'Bacon. I'm going for bacon,' he continued. 'Although I'm going to ask for the head to be returned whole. They shrink wrap it in cling film and send it back to you. It'll keep in the freezer for ages.'

The bell ended our session by the time he'd finished his tips for trotters. We smiled awkwardly and both tried to pretend we hadn't just seen each other tick 'no'.

My next date arrived. He was in his late forties, scruffily bearded and balding, but had made an effort. The crease across his nipples and belly button proved his new shirt was fresh out of the packet.

'I am a British Rail timetable specialist,' he began, in answer to my, 'So, what do you do?' line of questioning. 'But, by the way,' he added rapidly. 'There's something you need to know.'

'Yes?' I wondered if I was going to get an exclusive on the West Coast Mainline.

He leaned forward, looking worried. 'I've just looked at my entry on the Speed Dater website and it says "bisexual" on my profile.' He whispered the bisexual bit. 'I think I may have ticked the wrong box when I filled out the forms. So if you go up on the website to put your results in tomorrow, that's what it will say. But I'm not,' he said. 'Please do not allow that entry to influence your opinion on me.'

'You're *not* bisexual?' I asked loudly.

'No, no. Not bisexual,' he muttered, staring furtively around.

'Ah, right,' I said. And wrote, 'not bisexual' clearly on his notes, so he could see I had understood that and taken it into account.

I paused. Then couldn't resist. 'Ever thought of trying it though?'

'Err . . . No,' said Timetable Man.

'Ever done anything unusual? Threesomes?'

He blinked at me in confusion. 'Is that what you want then?' he asked.

'No,' I started. 'No, sorry, it's just force of habit to ask.'

'Oh.'

The bell eventually cut into the silence and again, we both smiled and pretended we'd said 'yes'.

A stream of men continued.

'What do you do for a living then?' they'd ask.

'I'm a tabloid journalist.'

'Oh. Are you friends with lots of famous people then?'

'No, I'm not,' I'd say.

And I'd tell them what the day job involved.

'Okay, Speed Daters!' *Speed Dating Leader Tony!* had shouted joyously after an hour. 'Click on the website tomorrow morning, enter in your "yes" ticks, and you will get a *full* list of everyone who also ticked "yes" for you. Then it's up to you who you want to get in touch with and, hey! Take it all further! Thank you for Speed Dating everyone! I hope you had a really *grrreat* night.' He said the 'grrreat' bit like Tony the Tiger in the Frosties advert, and gave a little playful tiger paw move as he did it.

At 9.01 am I went onto the website, clicked onto the profiles, and entered a few 'yes' ticks.

Four hours later my results arrived. Nobody had ticked 'yes'. Nobody. Absolutely nobody. No one had even ticked 'Just a Friend'. Not even Train Timetable Man, who, I noted, was still bisexual.

I also had an email from *Speed Dating Leader Tony!* Not a date offer though. Oh no. Merely a standard email reminding me that I was 'fully entitled to a free event'. Yes. Because I'd clearly been so crap on the last one, hadn't I?

Of course it was worded more kindly than that. It had exclamation marks and lots of excitement about an upcoming 'Speed Dating and Wine Event!' that I may like to pay £50 for, and a reminder that, 'our average match rate is a WHOPPING 85%. That means that 85% of our clients meet at least one person that they mutually click with and want to see again!'

Which meant, statistically speaking, that I was in the 15 per cent who were clinically proven to be so crap they couldn't even bloody pull at speed dating.

I had just been scientifically confirmed as an absolute loser.

Okay, so now I was starting to get worried.

8

NIGHTS IN BLACK SPANDEX

And the Art of Covering Fetish Freaks

One morning I arrived in the office to find a reporter packing his belongings into a box. He'd worked at the paper for thirty years, and had once lunched regularly with Elizabeth Taylor and Richard Burton. He was unstoppable on the London social scene. I'd sat next to him on several occasions and would pass on phone messages from Joan Collins and Miss Taylor, and hear him going into whispered giggles on long, transatlantic calls with Hollywood A-listers. 'Oh, I won't write a *thing*,' he'd say. 'But God, what a *party*! How did she get it out in the end?'

But the reporting world moves on. Today's stars are not Hollywood legends who a reporter works hard with over the years to gain their trust. Today's stars are people who are being churned out by reality TV shows overnight. Or WAGs and ex-lovers who get rich quick from a revealing dress or an even more revealing kiss-and-tell. They are overnight celebrities and the way to report on them is to get in quick, open your chequebook and convince them to sell their soul.

The man, in his late fifties, was not built for banging on the doors, begging *Big Brother* stars for a quote. He wasn't built for the new quick-fame system and for pandering to its new stars. *'Don't worry. I won't write a thing,'* didn't fit into the modern tabloid system. He was called in before the 9 am Conference, given a year's pay-off and told to make way for a younger man.

He'd cleared his desk with dignity and left, before hardly anyone could notice he was crying.

'Dear oh dear, things are *not* going well,' said Robohack with a smirk. He'd been smirking since 9.03 am. Ever since he'd bagged the newly departed staff reporter's desk.

I'd stared at the floor as the departing reporter packed his desk. Both he and I knew that although outwardly I had made noises of concern and support, inwardly my heart had leapt. His leaving meant that, finally, a staff vacancy had emerged. After three years of shifting, with just vague promises of future employment and commitment, the finishing line was in sight. Myself and Robohack had clung on for months, seeing off – and in many cases, stitching up – all other shifters. Now one of us was to get the coveted staff reporter job.

Robohack had spent the previous night trailing around after a TV star and witnessing her late night visits to her drug dealer. 'Another splash in the bag, I'd say,' he smirked. 'Looks like that staff job which has just come up is mine.'

Crump had originally been put on the same story but had refused to turn over the dealer. 'Oh mate I can't,' he had wailed at the News Editor. 'It'd be like betraying *family*.'

'So, you got anything for The List?' smirked Robohack at me. 'The List' is the list of stories which are pitched to The Editor each day in Conference. Each reporter pitches their story to the section editor, who in turn then tries to convince The Editor it's a great idea and deserves to go in the paper.

The 'splash' is a front-page story. A 'spread', a two-page report. A 'top' is a short story which goes at the top of a column on one page. 'Back of the Book' refers to a report which makes it in, but is buried inside the paper. A 'nib' is a 'news in brief' – a short one hundred word story used as a space filler. A 'pup' is something which isn't going to be printed anywhere. Your contact has sold you a pup, swindled you, and the story has no bite. 'Tosser' is what the reporter is branded for trying to get this 'pup' into the newspaper.

All I had mustered that week were four nibs and a potential page lead on a former *Big Brother* star in a lesbian clinch. Newspapers are fed stories by freelancers who work for news agencies, and my news agency contact had assured me the pair had been out cavorting 'in secret' and he'd caught and photographed them 'unawares'. But, from the way both were in full make-up and just-stepped-out-of-the-salon hair (and clearly holding their stomachs in), it was all obviously a set-up by the pair in an attempt to get some cash. 'Pup,' smirked Robohack, cracking his knuckles as he prepared to type his splash.

Crump slumped in. It was 9.05 am. Conference was any

second now. Crump looked particularly rough. He was in last night's clothes. And last night's facial hair.

'Anything for The List?' said Anne, fingers poised over the keyboard. 'Last call for The List . . .'

'Hang on, I know I've got a bloody story somewhere . . .' said Crump, emptying his pockets. Out spilled various bits of paper, asthma inhalers, silver foil, Marlboro. He delved through all of them whilst attacking his chin with an electric razor.

'Conference!' came a growl from The Editor's office.

'Yup, yup, it's the splash. Hang on . . . just can't remember what it was,' scrabbled Crump, peering at his cigarette packs. 'World Exclusive. Got it late last night. Now what was it? Ah ha!' Crump brandished a beer mat aloft. He squinted at the scribbles covering it. 'That was it. TV star. On the old marching powder. Absolutely kosher. I'll have it bashed out by 10,' he sniffed. 'Can't reveal the old sources though.'

'Crump!' roared The Editor. 'Now!'

'Coming,' yelled Crump. Then sneezed.

'Damn,' he sighed, brushing frantically at the desk below him. 'Sixty quid's worth . . .'

And he swept the new List into Conference.

Crump turned out to have the superior coke-snorting story and emerged triumphant, minutes later.

The meeting went less well for me. The Editor had also had an idea for a story that morning, it emerged. Unfortunately it involved another den of iniquity. I was getting sick of the depravity already. I mean, I wasn't exactly on a par with Robert, who'd been buying prostitutes for twenty-five years, but it was all starting to get bloody tiresome. I was bored of bordellos. Incidentally, if you are also feeling a touch overwhelmed by all the debauchery being thrown my way, spare a thought for me. I was having to witness it. Oh, and rest assured that this is the last little whorehouse I had to visit.

For yes, once again, I was the sucker that got picked. As The Editor shot out of his bunker, I desperately leapt for the phone and started dialling my mobile in the old two-handset work-avoidance routine, but there was a tap on my shoulder and a Post-it note stuck to my forehead saying 'My office NOW'. I was on another vice job. Oh bollocks, I thought. And I had a date tonight as well. A nice maths teacher I'd met in a café during a rare alcohol-free day. I'd had high hopes for that one and had been very excited about Date One. Now I had to think of a decent excuse to give him, which didn't involve rubber.

It was to get worse. I was on the job with Robohack, oh joy. His story had been relegated to a few paragraphs on page seven as Crump's A-lister exposé had now taken over pages one to five.

'Oh, bad luck,' I said to Robohack.

'Oh, fuck off,' he replied.

Eight hours later he was still swearing at me.

'You did this deliberately, didn't you?' he said as I attempted to zip him into his 'alien seduction catsuit' in two-tone pearl-sheen pewter.

I *had* done it deliberately. I'd deliberately gone into a shop in Soho's Old Compton Street that morning, armed with

Robohack's measurements, and deliberately subtracted a centimetre from each as I asked for something in a 'snug fit'. The resultant outfit was roughly the size of a condom.

Mine, in matching Supatex with a purple hue, was marked as 'large' in the shop but also appeared minuscule once out the packet. The lady had insisted that some brute force and plenty of talc would get me into it. A full leg wax would have helped too, I had thought as I wrenched it on. I resolved never to only wax from the knee down any more.

By 4 pm I was sat in the 'hers' version of the catsuit, in the back of an old BT van outside a pub in Amersham on a summer's afternoon. I was hot. In retrospect, it had perhaps not been a good idea to put the outfit on at the start of the ninety-minute drive. (Plus a ten-minute wait outside a petrol station toilet.)

I was also having hearing difficulties. The 'hers' version came with a fetching fitted hood, which could be worn either down round the neck where it strangled you, or pulled up snugly around the ears. Once pulled up I was able to breathe in it which was a definite plus, but sound was muffled by both the layer of PVC and the two-tone colour-coordinated alien antennae sprouting from the top. It was billed as having 'sensuous style-lines' on the packet, I noted. Examining myself in the rearview mirror I realised I actually looked more like Tinky Winky from the *Teletubbies*.

Poor Robohack was not built for PVC either. Turned out the man had a continuous coat of hair from his head, all the way down his spine; although after forcing the zip to do up, he now had a few bald patches. I could hear his yelps even through my hood. Robohack, in his all-in-one, looked like the star of a very low-budget porn remake of *Batman*. The line of his Y-fronts was clearly on display. He was now sweating profusely and smelt vaguely of wet dog.

'You look fine,' I reassured him.

'Gah,' he gasped. 'Could you not have got something sleeveless?'

I shrugged. I had got better at Investigations over the months, but reminded him that as yet, I was still technically a shifting trainee and therefore still learning about gentlemen's S&M tailoring issues.

We were both to carry a camera. Mine was to be in the handbag – which actually set off the whole Tinky Winky theme nicely. Robohack donned the rigged leather jacket favoured by male reporters. We wired his hidden camera into his back zip, then through into the jacket, with its lens disguised as a button hole. The jacket hid some of the VPL, I assured him, but he remained miserable and itchy, which I was secretly pleased about.

Leather and rubber do not a comfortable combination make. 'I'm sweating bloody cobs here,' Robohack moaned from the back of the van, crouched on all fours as he tried, unsuccessfully, to readjust his trouser department for comfort.

Our latest dressing up stunt was, of course, The Editor's idea.

'Someone's just rung in and blown the whistle on a kinky school-ma'am,' he had rasped from behind his desk as I was called into his inner lair. 'Apparently she's running undercover sex parties for fetish freaks.

'She's giving lessons in the three Rs – reading, writing . . .

and rubber. To girls, guys, gimps and any other thing beginning with "g" you can think of that the public will be shocked by.'

'Grannies?' I suggested.

He whirled on, 'I want her photographed, interviewed and fully exposed over a page 12–13 spread.'

'It is,' he thundered as he flung open the door, 'the corruption of our innocents. Children are the future and she should not be teaching them.

'Dress code latex.'

I heard Crump wince as I passed. 'Ow. *Terrible* chafing,' he had murmured in sympathy.

Investigations journalism is an odd thing. Undercover police officers undergo months of training, and are wired up to the gills with tracking equipment and SWAT teams and things. Donal MacIntyre might think he was being all tough, going round council estates and getting mugged and having tattoos done to impress football thugs, but he also had a full production back-up team. In the SAS they train for months, running over mountains with just a packet of nuts for dinner and learning all sorts of surveillance techniques before they start any job.

Us undercover hacks were basically told to go out, find a fancy dress outfit, and get on with it.

Our destination was a converted pub in a backstreet of Amersham. It was late-afternoon. Broad daylight. Once Robo-hack was dressed we squelched into the sunshine from the car park to a side door, where people were queuing politely. They were all patiently waiting for their Three Rs tutorial.

Sensibly, they had hidden their latex splendour under long duffel coats. So, apart from various oddly coloured shiny legs poking out underneath, they all looked pretty normal.

It was different inside. A gentleman, dressed in spandex cowboy chaps and no trousers, greeted us from the shadows of the doorway, ushering us in and down a darkened staircase, where we were politely offered a cloakroom service at £1 a piece. More people queued politely and duffel coats were removed, as were normal standards of decorum as acres of straining latex was revealed. People had not only gone for sleeveless, we noted, they'd gone for backless, frontless and bottomless too. And, we realised, we weren't the only two who had struggled to make things fit. People rolled past in outfits which strained at their rubber seams. 'God, it's like a Dunlop tyre factory,' murmured Robohack. And we watched with interest as one party goer demonstrated they were, indeed, inflatable.

We were moved into a side room and informed we were about to be frisked. I was unfazed. I had been on enough of these jobs by now to figure out how to overcome this little hurdle. Should you ever find yourself in the position of having to carry a hidden camera into a fetish party, then simply secrete the camera in a handbag with a false mesh side that it can film through. Then arrange a bright scarf over the top, and over the top of that, throw in a layer of tampons. Then head for the male Security guard. The bag was opened, and hastily handed back, with a shudder, by Security. Women's things. Works every time. These S&M Security men can stomach the rudest, seediest and most painfully erotic of sexual acts, but go to pieces at the sight of Bodyform.

Robohack was more thoroughly frisked, but the camera, hidden under the layers of the rubber suit and jacket, stayed undetected as he smiled winningly and winsomely to distract security.

'Aren't you hot?' said the Chaps chap to him. 'Don't you need the disrobing room?' Robohack growled that he did not. He couldn't take off the jacket, or several yards of wire and a camera would drop out.

A drop of water rolled down his forehead, but he squelched out of the room and into the party, bravely insisting that he was 'just fine'. I made sure I videoed him. On an undercover job with a colleague, roughly half the tape should be dedicated to getting the story, and the other half to getting as many embarrassing pictures of your co-worker in rubber fetish gear as you can, which should then be shown round the office on your return.

In we ploughed. Into a nightclub where a man in an all-in-one rubber Dalmatian outfit was on all fours. He had, I realised, definitely made the extra effort. He'd gone made-to-measure in every spot.

Mr Dalmatian grabbed Robohack's leg as we passed. I made sure I filmed that for later. Maybe it was the scent of wet dog that attracted him, I thought. And that stitching on the dog outfit was *spectacular*, I mused. I suddenly felt self-conscious of my one-size-fits-all, off-the-peg number. My fetish party equivalent of Primark, shown up by his couture. Robohack kicked the dog off. 'Sod off,' he grunted and then added the same to me, as he caught the angle of my handbag.

'*Hello* there,' minced a man dressed in a white lace-effect (rubber, naturally) baby-doll outfit. He too had only gone for

144

half a leg on the shaving department, I noticed. A sartorial no-no when his hirsute thighs were teamed with matching white stockings and high heels.

'I'm a civil servant by day,' he said, and formally shook hands. 'By night . . . whatever you want me to be.' He spun on his white stilettos in an attractive showgirl style, as he tossed back his shoulders and shimmied with jazz hands.

He muttered something else to me. Sounded like 'Iraq'. 'What?' I yelled back. I knew this whole thing was run by a teacher, but still, I couldn't believe I was expected to have a conversation about international politics. 'I don't know too much about it,' I shouted. 'But Iraq . . . oh yes, it's all bad. Very bad.' Oh God. I couldn't believe my lack of current affairs nous meant I couldn't even converse with trannies at dungeon parties.

I tried to read every paper in the morning, but typically spent more time discussing *Heat* magazine than the *Guardian*, to be honest. I gestured that I couldn't really hear anything under my hooded antennae and over what I think was Kajagoogoo's *Too Shy*, which was by now pounding out from the basement speakers. Mr Baby-doll gestured towards the centre of the room, where a middle-aged man wearing a giant blonde wig had climbed on a wooden rack and was being thrashed by another man in black lingerie.

'A rack,' he repeated, with a smile. Clearly he wanted to join in.

'Oh *a rack*!' I beamed. With relief. 'No, no. First time. Just watching. Shy.' I shrugged. 'Too shy, shy.'

'Freaks,' snarled Robohack, as we slunk away. 'Now, where's the girl? I need to get out of here.'

With only half an hour of battery life left in the cameras, we prowled the room for our 'target', downed a couple of vodkas for courage, and asked various people in various bulging outfits if they'd seen the hostess. As ever at these do's, people were unfailingly polite, courteous and helpful, straining their eyes through the sea of undulating rubber and their voices over the *Now That's What I Call Music 8!* compilation to try and help. Eventually we found the kinky ma'am overseeing the proceedings from near the buffet table. She arranged egg sandwiches and shouted directions to a heavily built woman in a black G-string, who was being tied to a wooden cross.

We waited, politely, for some bottom thrashing to stop and then, with twenty minutes of life left, our 'interviews' started. 'We're new and we don't know what to do,' I began with a smile, accepting the proffered boiled egg refreshment. 'So. Do you come here often?'

It was a straightforward confessional job. The footage was quickly in the can – the teacher confessed to running the secret club behind the school's back, and provided an inform-ative lecture about the use of household implements to spice up a marriage. Across the room, Mr Baby-doll was just taking his place on the rack. Being the perfect party hostess, the school ma'am pointed out a fresh delivery of sausage rolls and then explained what exactly was on offer in her dungeon.

It was all in the bag five minutes later. Enough for a two-page spread with explanatory diagrams and photos. We could make our excuses and leave. I was desperate for the loo though, and asked Robohack for a quick pitstop before we left – my outfit being not entirely suitable for popping into the local service station on the way back to the office. He tutted at me. 'Be quick.'

I heaved myself into the ladies, smiled nervously – but in no way invitingly – at a queue of various lingerie-clad party goers, who were making small talk about small outfits. I carefully disrobed in the narrow cubicle. Undressing is not an easy task when you're peeling off a rubber catsuit. It's even harder when combined with a hidden microphone and camera, whose contents you know will be handed round the newsdesk later. I placed the handbag onto the floor, pointed it at the wall so it couldn't see anything, and sang loudly so it couldn't hear anything as I clawed at the PVC.

After twenty minutes – these all-in-one suits are *not* practical, especially when you haven't packed any talcum powder – I met up with Robohack, who was now hopping from foot to foot. 'Come on,' he shouted into my antennae over Duran Duran's *Wild Boys*. 'She keeps coming over saying she wants to demonstrate something with Ikea shelf parts.'

'Yeah, we've got enough haven't we? Corruption? Rubber?' I shouted back, cheerfully. 'Plus that spirited thrashing she's just handed out to Mr Baby-doll on the rack suggests her disability claims are a bit dodgy. Put that in.'

Robohack was shaking his head, 'No!' he said.

Creep. Who did he think he was? Okay he'd had a few decent tip offs, but I was the one who'd been slogging my guts out on Investigations for months now and this was hardly my first vice job. 'Don't be stupid, it's a perfectly decent angle,' I shouted, as I began to root round in my handbag under the Tampax for our car keys. 'Come on. Benefits-cheat teacher whips her private pupils into shape. You'll never guess what

147

the Dickens she gets up to at the weekend. King Leer. No Holds Bard. That's a double-page spread, I'm telling you!'

'No!' he repeated, yanking my arm. Muttering something else which was unintelligible. Sounded like *stupid cow*.

'I know what I'm doing,' I shouted back over *Club Tropicana*'s opening bars.

Suddenly I felt my rubber antenna being yanked from behind. It was the Dalmatian. He was behind me. He'd risen up on his hind legs.

I stood, momentarily transfixed, before Robohack penetrated my hood with a, 'What are you *doing*?' and yanked me out the door.

'*Are you reporters*?' Mr Dalmatian howled.

Mr Baby-doll sat up on the rack. '*What the fuck* . . .?' he started. It was no language for ladies' lingerie.

We legged it.

We only just made it to the van. My exit was fully impeded by my thigh-length boots and the exit stairway. The boots don't bend at the knees and are a bugger when you're going upstairs at speed. God knows how Julia Roberts did it in *Pretty Woman*. I looked like an extra from a Zombie movie as I hobbled, stiff-legged, to the safety of the waiting van.

Mr Dalmatian ran through the club after us, but fortunately his dog habits (combined with his taut tailoring) did not extend to him chasing vans up the street.

'Fucking idiot!' yelled Robohack, as we left, clawing his rubber chest open as he drove. 'You fucking tosser! What the fuck was *that*, you fuckwit?'

You know, sometimes I wondered if they were too hasty sacking that shifter with Tourettes all those years ago.

Crump's drugs splash got him promoted to Showbiz Editor.

Robohack got the staff reporter job.

I got a bollocking.

Not a full scale one. No football. No broken bones. But I wish I'd kept the rubber hood on.

I returned, ashen-faced, to my desk ten minutes later and sat in the shadows of Investigations, folding my alien seduction catsuit into a drawer, and staring with envy at the ladies on the Royal desk, who were lit by sunlight. They were in knee-length florals, or pastels. So much more forgiving. So much less flammable. So much more acceptable in Lancastrian Tesco aisles.

I stopped staring. Went to sob in the nearby loos at the futility of life for a bit, then came back to see if it all looked any better. It didn't.

I had been on the paper for years now. Years of shifting. And no contract in sight. I looked at my diary. I was due at another fetish party the next day. Friday involved a bent copper who needed exposing for selling himself on the internet, offering ladies 'passionate sex sessions with full genuine police uniform. And handcuffs'. I was to go along with a girl from the Crime Desk called Lucy, pretend it was her Hen Night and demand to see his truncheon. On the floor was a sign advertising a dogging site, which The Editor had caught sight of on the A13 that morning, as he'd been chauffeur-driven in to the office. He had ordered the driver to stop and reverse, leapt out and personally wrenched it loose, before holding it triumphantly aloft as he came into the newsroom that morning.

My life was now being dictated by lampposts. Whilst I'd been away crying, there had been two phone messages. One from the teacher I was due to go on a date with saying he wasn't interested in playing games any more. Another one about a massage parlour. Where the staff regularly entertained a foot-baller who apparently was still interested in playing games. As long as they involved a bullwhip.

I couldn't hack it any more, I suddenly realised. I hated Investigations. I couldn't take any more of the shadows. I'd had enough. I'd quit in the morning, I decided. Go back home. Move back to my old single bed. My parents would no doubt greet me with open arms and relief that they were able to cancel their tabloid subscription, stop worrying what the neighbours thought and revert to buying the *Telegraph* once more. I could buy some nice Laura Ashley frocks and maybe meet someone nice. I could give up smoking. I had failed. I'd had enough. I couldn't take it. I gave up.

Meanwhile, I thought, I may as well get drunk. I may as well end my tabloid career where it started. With alcohol. I headed to the pub.

Crump was there. Celebrating.

'What's wrong?' he asked, after clocking the two bottles of wine I had sucked in a silent fury. I told him about all the latex and the lampposts.

'Look, forget Investigations. Why not come and do shifts on the Showbiz desk?' he suggested. 'Department of Silly Stories. I'm now the head of Silly Stories. I can do the hiring.

'We make it fit. We make it fast. We make it up. That's our motto.'

So, I didn't quit. And a week later I started on the Showbiz desk. And finally, after over three years of flailing around in brothels, I found my niche in newspapers. I loved Showbiz. I found it the most fascinating and exhilarating of newspaper beats. It's also where life started to get really strange. Within months, I was kidnapping Very Famous Lesbians and hassling The Hoff.

9

MY JADE GOODY KIDNAP

And the Art of the Newspaper Buy-Up

Domestos was in disgrace again the morning I kidnapped the Very Famous Lesbian.

The night before, he'd filed two thousand words on how a TV actor had finally quit the booze. Half an hour after finishing the interview, he'd told the star that 'just one won't hurt, will it?' The pair had duly gone for 'just one' to 'celebrate' finishing the interview. It was just a shame that a rival paper printed a photograph of the star, blind drunk and exiting a bar, on the same day that our paper had printed the interview claiming he was now a 'yoga loving angel'. Domestos was just visible in the back of the shot in the rival paper. He was horizontal.

'Bloody Domestos,' said The Editor the next day. 'Kills 99.9% of all known stories. Dead.'

In fairness, Domestos had merely been doing his job. He was trying to 'hold' his story.

There is an art to tabloid success, which changes depending on whether you work on a daily or Sunday newspaper. On a daily paper it is all about a quick response to a story. Grab the facts, bash out the story as quickly as possible and get it in the paper and out to the public as fast as you can. Or 'file by three and in the pub for tea', as one News Editor I knew used to shout across the office as deadline loomed.

So that's the trick on a daily. Often it's a one-fact story. Girl gets dumped. Race to doorstep of girl. Take photo of girl. File that she looks 'sad' or 'brave' or 'grim-faced' or 'devastated', add a bit of colour about what she's wearing and you've got yourself a page-lead which sails into the paper the next day. With some celebs, like Jennifer Aniston for example, papers have been doing that same story every day for years.

But sometimes, when there's a big story or a big buy-up, the skill is different. If you've spent thousands on a buy-up, you may choose to run a story over several days. Or hold the timing of its release to ensure it makes maximum impact. Or you may have to sit on a story for days, weeks even, until legal problems are resolved. So the trick is to get the story and 'hold' it, keep it secret. Make sure that no other reporter in the country can get their hands on it. Sunday papers work like this all the time. The working days in a Sunday newspaper newsroom are from Tuesday to Saturday, with the journalists taking Sunday and Monday as their weekend. Hardly any news stories ever happen on a Saturday – certainly not enough to fill twenty pages of a newspaper. So the trick is to find a story early in the week and tie it up as your exclusive, and then sit on it all week before whacking it in the paper.

The problem is, with the rest of Fleet Street all fighting for stories, how do you keep your exclusive an exclusive? How do you find a story on a Tuesday and keep everyone from finding out about it until you're able to print it five days later? How can you stop everyone from going to the person's doorstep and nicking your story?

Well, one of the easiest ways this is done is to simply kidnap people.

And this is what I did with Jade Goody's mum.

Some celebs disappoint slightly in the flesh. I spent six years as a Showbiz hack and met all manner of people along the way. I once had a three-hour meeting with Johnny Rotten and was thoroughly looking forward to drunken carnage, but he insisted on cuddling his wife and asking if there was any-thing I could think of to help him save an endangered koala bear he'd just met.

Some are fabulous. Tony Curtis pinched my bottom when I passed him in a corridor once, despite being in a wheelchair at the time. And some are great when they're angry. Hugh Grant once chased a man from the *Mirror* across several muddy fields when he spotted him skulking at the back of a wedding party trying to see who Hugh was snogging. When he finally caught up with the reporter a couple of furlongs later, Hugh sank to his knees and beseeched him, 'Give up. For the love of God. Would you. Please. Just. Give up.'

'It was *brilliant*,' said the reporter in the pub that night. 'It was just like being in that opening scene in *Four Weddings and a Funeral*.'

When the soap goddess Maggie Jones passed away recently, I couldn't resist a chuckle remembering one encounter I'd had with the *Coronation Street* star who'd brought the acerbic Blanche Hunt to life so brilliantly.

I'd gone up to Manchester to do cast interviews and Maggie was sitting outside a church during a long, involved wedding scene for her co-stars, having her customary cigarette and catching up with the day's tabloid news. Unfortunately, the front pages contained a rather unfortunate revelation about a star from a rival soap.

'Dearheart,' she said, waving me over and brandishing the paper at me. 'You work on these paper things, don't you? Tell me. What's dogging?'

I took a deep breath and duly filled her in. There was a pause. She raised a solo eyebrow, and drily declared, 'In my day we just went to the cinema.'

I had a great time with some celebs. I stroked Johnny Depp's beard and offered him a snog (he declined but said 'bless you'), I fondled Superman's biceps, shared a bed with Suzi Quatro (long story, we were sharing a house with someone who was clinically insane and Suzi's was the only room with a lock on the door) and I got blindingly drunk and danced round Joan Collins at Christopher Biggins's fabulous sixtieth birthday bash. I also once spent a highly entertaining half hour perched outside Peter Andre's hotel room in Australia, during the first night he and Jordan spent together out of the jungle, with me and a snapper both stifling giggles as we listened to the seduction scene through the walls.

And I can't help giggling too at the memory of a fuming Cilla Black exclaiming, 'How did you get in here?!' as I pitched up at her dressing room door, just five minutes after she quit *Blind Date* on live TV. That was a lucky one, actually. I was in a nearby bar when a friend, who was working on the show, texted me to say Cilla had just unexpectedly announced the news live on air. I broke in through a back fire escape, where I roamed around the ITV building until I saw a sign saying 'dressing rooms'. Luckily, half the ITV production staff were so hacked off with her, they let me pass and even pointed directions to her door. 'Be my guest,' said one. 'If she tells you what she's playing at, then please come back and let us know too.' I arrived at her room, swung open the door, and started the interview just five minutes after she'd got off the telly. She stood there, champagne glass in hand, a little shocked at the sudden, unexpected arrival of this impertinent hack demanding a personal and immediate press conference. Pity ... in the heat of the moment I totally forgot to say 'Surprise, Surprise!'

But my favourite, my absolute favourite celebrity encounter of all time was Jade Goody. Which is odd. Because our meeting started with me kidnapping her mother.

Let me explain what I was doing.

Big Brother fever had overtaken the country. This was the third series, before it all got a bit dull and full of complete wannabes, and Jade was at the heart of the programme. This was the first time she appeared in the House. She had no idea what life was about to throw at her or what impact she was having outside. Jade, back then, was a non-celebrity, just an ordinary girl from Bermondsey. She had no agent, and no clue about how the press and the whole showbiz system works. She'd gone in the House for a laugh, and hoped she might win the cash prize at the end; meanwhile she was having a whale of a time in the house getting drunk and having the odd duvet dive with the men. She was totally oblivious to the fact that outside, unbeknownst to her, she was getting an absolute mauling from the papers.

'Jade the Pig!' shouted newspaper headlines. Kiss-and-tells had been unearthed from unsavoury exes. And I admit I was as bad as everyone else. I'd gone to try and talk to her previous boyfriend the week before. The young tattooed gentleman had answered the door stark naked, set his dog on me (bit of a recurring event for me, that) and yelled obscenities through the window at me from his graffiti covered home as I left. I had taken that as a 'no'.

'Go and see the mother,' was The Editor's brilliant idea in Conference one morning. Jackiey (yes, an 'i', an 'e' *and* a 'y' – I've spent hours arguing over that one with the Subs) was also getting bad press. Descriptions were basically a variation on 'one-armed lesbian former crack-head'. It was not a doorstep I was looking forward to, to be honest. There were vague rumours of a ferocious guard dog lurking inside the house.

But round I went to Bermondsey. I wore high heels and a low blouse, just in case I was her type. Dressing for doorsteps is one of the skills you are taught as a female reporter. There was one Showbiz Editor who was renowned for turning up on men's doorsteps in a see-through blouse and just-been-in-bed hair. We female reporters would all put on our highest heels in the hope we would impress. Jackiey got the full shoe treatment and I put on my best smile, and knocked. She shot out of the door, dog in hot pursuit. Jackiey very definitely had two arms, I noticed, and one of them was raised in a fist.

God, the more I look at it now, the more I realise that my journalism course really didn't cover the essentials. It certainly hadn't covered how to deal with doorsteps like this.

I screamed. And started to shake uncontrollably. I'd taken flowers – I always took flowers to doorsteps. Bringing gifts to a door is a classic tabloid tactic. If you take flowers then, as the person answers the door, they are obliged to say thank you and wait for you to hand them over. This gives you a twenty second period of grace to chat to them and try and get them to talk as you slowly hand over the goodies. Even if all you get from them is a 'no comment', the flowers give you another chance. The trick is to smile understandingly, say you quite understand that it's all so bewildering, but please accept the flowers as an apology for interrupting them, and should you be able to help in any way, or if they change their mind, your card is attached.

Letters requesting interviews, no matter how polite, tend to be binned. But flowers are friendly. They tend to be kept, and put on display in living rooms. People in the tabloid eye tend to be bombarded by several papers in a day and, after a few days of this, will often decide the best way to stop all the people coming round is to just have a chat with one of them. When sitting around in their living room wondering which of the press they should talk to, the flowers would sit on the shelf as a large friendly, floral hint that the winner should be me.

But Jackiey didn't look in the mood to chat. My lilies started to nervously drip pollen on the doormat to her Bermondsey flat. Her dog sort of grimaced, too, as it stood guard.

'Which paper are you from?' demanded Jackiey. 'Are you the one that's just called my daughter a pig?'

'No!' I squawked.

'Oh God, sorry then,' she grinned. 'I thought it was them back again. You okay love? Don't worry about the dog. He's harmless.

'Nice trotters,' she added. Pointing at my feet.

Months later I was to ask Jackiey why she invited me inside at that point – the only journalist she allowed across her doorstep when Jade was in the *Big Brother* House. 'You were shaking like a bloody leaf,' she said, 'I thought you might faint on the doorstep. And besides. I needed a shower and wanted someone to get me the towels out of the cupboard. And you're tall.'

So, half an hour later, I found myself in the bizarre position of joining Jackiey at the heart of the media storm that was starting to surround her. And interviewing her through a shower curtain.

Incidentally, Jackiey was not to be the last person to start suggesting grievous bodily harm. It sort of comes with the territory when you're a journalist. I've already mentioned the pop star who wanted to break my legs, but more on that later. There was a transsexual who wanted to kill me, too. And a cross-dressing bank manager I met in a dungeon once who was absolutely fuming at me. Like I said. That's just how the job goes sometimes.

Anyway. Back to Jackiey, who had definitely agreed not to punch me at this point, so the doorstep was going well. And I was at the beginning of my week with the woman who did, and does still, constantly find herself being attacked as a monster in the papers. And I was about to find out that I rather like her.

Spend a bit of time with Jackiey and you'll realise she's no monster. Yes, she swears like a trooper. Yes, she has a habit of trying to hit people by swinging her paralysed arm at them, and yes, she can go into an absolute tailspin of fury at times. And there was that afternoon when I had to make a lot of apologies in a hairdressing salon for hairdryers and insults flying through the air. But I've worked with worse.

And I think, underneath all that, Jackiey is just an ordinary woman who is and was always fiercely protective of her daughter. She's the only person in Jade's life who never saw her as a cash cow. She never sold out on her.

Jackiey had much to be protective about at the time. Jade-hating and Jade-baiting had become a national sport. The twenty-year-old girl from South London was being branded 'Michelin girl', a 'sex-crazed, lying, two-timing drunken tart' and a 'pig'. My own paper had been hurling abuse too.

Jade's mother had lived through this, alone, in her Bermondsey flat, and had to watch and read as the papers crucified her daughter for sport; the same papers that knocked on her door demanding interviews days later. I began to be very glad I'd been chased by dogs during my own attempt at kiss-and-telling. Jackiey was pretty angry. I wouldn't like to cross her. Ever.

But she was upset too. In fact, she burst into tears shortly after I crossed the doorstep. 'This is my little girl they're talking about,' she said, pointing at the pile of newspapers in the hall, full of insults about her daughter. 'I'm terrified for her when she comes out. She's a good girl, but she's going to get lynched. I'll kill those reporters.'

I sat there saying sorry a lot. There were a few times as a tabloid hack that I had my eyes opened to what we were actually doing. Usually, the whole momentum of the newsroom carries you along. This person is evil. This one is good. This one is right. This one is wrong. And the copy is written to match. It's when you meet the person behind the headlines that sometimes you suddenly realise the hysteria you've created is all wrong. Our paper had been running stuff too. Not nice stuff. I put a call in to the desk to see if any more Not Nice Stuff was planned. 'Not if you get the mum,' I was told. 'Not if you get the chat with Jade.'

Suddenly, like the rest of Fleet Street, the paper was executing a guilty U-turn as it realised that the whole nation had fallen in love with Jade. And no matter who won, she was the one that they wanted on the cover. From now on, I was told to promise Jackiey, the paper is on Jade's side. Talk to us, and we're Team Jade.

I wasn't the only one promising that. I'd arrived at 8 am. By the time I looked out the door half-an-hour later, there was a fleet of cars outside her flat, with snappers' lenses trained on the windows. Okay, now *I* know most of the pack are alcoholic misfits with disastrous social lives, but to an outsider the media in full flow is quite a terrifying sight. It's like a mass lynching mob, with a faceless stream of flashbulbs. The doorbell had started to ring. Reporters were starting to queue up outside and shout through the letterbox. A bouquet of flowers – twice the size of the one I'd bought her – was delivered by a reporter from the *Sunday People*. Bollocks. I wasn't the only one trying that trick. And it looked like their budgets were bigger.

Unfortunately for them, it was me that answered the door to take the blooms. I grabbed the flowers, said thanks very much and slammed the door in the face of the reporter who was stood there, demanding I moved aside so he could see Jackiey. I carefully removed his card from the flowers, before handing them to Jackiey and lying through my teeth saying, 'They're from some reporter. Didn't leave his name. Or a card. Odd.'

Jackiey was peering through from the net curtains at the reporter who was still standing on the doorstep. He was wearing a tailored three-piece suit. I knew the hack, I'd worked with him before. Daddy was someone very influential in newspapers and there were rumours he had his own trust fund. Hence the tailor.

'Is that a waistcoat he's wearing?' said Jackiey. 'God, he's going to get his head kicked in if he wears that around here,' she commented, watching as he started door-to-door enquiries across the council estate. Another bouquet arrived. The *Sunday Mirror* this time. It was even bigger. From a bloke called Kevin. I took them and said thanks to the delivery boy, and took them inside binning Kevin's card on the way.

'More flowers, no card,' I shrugged. 'Maybe it was the people who wrote "Kill the Pig", and they're trying to say sorry.'

Yes, I know. I was being A Lying Cow. But I had to get the story.

The press pack grew. 'They won't leave,' said Jackiey, looking out at them. 'I've had enough.'

The reason I think Jackiey was a much better mother than any of us gave her credit for is this: I was there on the day. I saw the press. I heard the journalists shout through the door. Not all of them were stupid enough to leave a message with me. They yelled through the glass that there were armfuls of cash on offer. Now Jackiey was not, it was fair to say, that well off. She and Jade shared a mattress in the one-bedroom flat. Their beloved, but highly flatulent 'guard' dog lived in there too. The cash on offer outside was life-changing. It could have bought her council flat outright and much more besides. But she was flatly refusing to take any of it. She'd promised Jade she wouldn't talk about her or do anything until Jade came out of the *Big Brother* House, and she was sticking to it. And the thing I admire about her is that she always did stick to it. She didn't let Jade down.

'I'm not talking. I ain't betraying her,' she said. 'Jade said not to sell anything to the press before she came out, so I won't.'

So we struck a deal right then and there, sitting in her living room with a windy dog as the press hammered on the windows. Jackiey would do an interview. But it would only run when Jade come out of *Big Brother* and then only if Jade had approved and read every word. If Jade didn't want it to go in, then it wouldn't. The money for the chat would be huge, as big as anything else on offer outside. More. We had budgets to burn on this one. Jade was the story of the year. 'Jade gets every bit of the wonga,' said Jackiey. 'I ain't taking nothing.'

It was a deal, I said. Like every hack who goes on a potential buy-up, I had letter-headed paper with me, and a blank contract. I wrote out the terms. I signed it. The chat was on.

At this point Jackiey looked out the window again. 'What about that lot?' she said. The press pack had now swelled to about twenty reporters.

'Ah,' I said. For I knew the answer to this bit. I'd just been briefed by The Editor. 'I'm afraid I'm going to have to kidnap you.'

Removing an interview subject from their home during a buy-up is a classic tabloid practice if you want to 'hold' the story. I would have to hold this story until Jade came out of the House, so it was essential for me to move Jackiey somewhere where she couldn't be tracked down. If you leave someone in their home, you make it easy for rival papers to find them, and therefore easy for rival reporters to butt in and steal your story. If it's a big story that everyone's after, then rival papers will stop at nothing to get it.

They sit outside, listen through doors and peer through windows, follow people down the street, ring their doorbells and call their phones until they get a line or a picture they can use. No hack, if they can avoid it, agrees to an interview sitting in a house when there are rival newspaper reporters outside. The rivals won't just stand there silently and let you get on with it. They'll shout through the letterbox. Brand you a liar, a fraud, yell that they'll pay double the money for the story . . . anything. Envelopes were already starting to drop through the letterbox and insults through the walls.

They were not going to give up. Hacks will sleep outside houses for days, waiting for a chance to steal your story.

There was one who worked for six days, guarding and persuading a showbiz couple to tell their story. He popped out for five minutes one morning only to arrive back to find a rival journalist sitting in the living room. The hack had smoothly sat down, claimed the other reporter was violently hungover from the previous night and they just needed to, 'check a few facts for the story' whilst the other one 'was throwing up'. He was thrown out, but not before he had managed to extract enough 'clarifying' quotes out of them to run a front page splash and three page 'spoiler' in his own paper, for free, the next day.

So the trick is to get the interviewee somewhere where no one will find them. It's no use letting them stay with friends or relatives – they'll all get doorstepped too and your buy-up will be tracked down within hours. To avoid all this, the best thing to do is get the subject out of their home, and hide them somewhere: i.e. kidnap them.

It's fun though, I told Jackiey as she packed a bag. Because we're going to kidnap you into a five-star hotel. 'Okay then,' she said.

We left five minutes later, nearly knocking over four paparazzi with my Nissan Micra as we sped off. Jackiey shot the waiting press pack a two-fingered salute as she left. I did too. Insults rang in my ears from the press pack, as they realised their story had just left the building.

An hour of some dramatic and probably entirely unnecessary screeching round corners and telling Jackiey to duck down in the back of the car so she couldn't be seen later, we drew into the car park at Selfridges Hotel. A besuited Crump was waiting in our pre-booked hotel room with a pre-booked bottle of champagne on ice. He introduced himself to Jackiey as 'her personal bodyguard' and announced that they were off for some 'serious shopping' as compensation for all this 'kidnapping malarky'. It's important in these buy-ups to keep the subject absolutely happy, and on side, and Jackiey, I'm happy to say, proved adept at taking to the full five-star treatment. MPs ain't got nothing on what this girl can buy when given full access to a newspaper's expenses account. She hit Chanel, armed with Crump and his corporate credit card.

I must admit, although undeniably fun for her, this wasn't just an act of generosity from the newspaper – it was a purely mercenary move. Our job was not only to keep Jackiey on side and get an interview. It was to get Jade on side, too. Jade was the hottest story in Britain at this point, and when she emerged from the *Big Brother* House, she would inevitably be faced with a choice of who she wanted to sell her story too. The paper that won the buy-up would put on thousands of readers in circulation as a result.

People in crisis will often turn to their families and those they trust for advice as they face a bewildering choice. When Jade came out of *Big Brother*, she was going to face a media maelstrom and would be shell-shocked at her return to reality. After seeing just a handful of people for months on end, she would be confronted with a crowd of hundreds screaming her name, a live TV appearance and oceans of newsprint analysing her, all of which had been printed over the past three months without her knowledge. She would be hauled in front of the world's press for an interview at around 2 am in the morning and then, at about 4 am, locked in a hotel room, surrounded by strange PRs and TV executives and told that nine national newspapers, five magazines and several TV channels were all prepared to pay hundreds of thousands of pounds for the exclusive rights to her story and which did she want to go with? For a dental assistant on less than £10,000 a year, it was a big, bewildering question.

Only one person who she trusted would be allowed in to speak to her at this point. And that person was her mother. If we had Jackiey's trust and had shown her a whale of a time, then the likelihood was she'd help convince Jade to go with our paper.

Cunning? Yes. Calculating? Absolutely. But it was a blow that we sweetened with couture and an expenses account, and Jackiey absolutely didn't mind.

'It's no expense spared,' the News Editor had declared, on hearing the most hunted woman in Britain was out of her house and now under our house arrest. 'Make her happy and make her talk.'

He had picked the right team for the job. Crump and Jackiey dashed back into the hotel, half-an-hour later, laden with designer carrier bags. Crump swung into operation on room service and ordered half the menu with a whisky chaser. Operation Keep the Goodys Happy was in full swing.

We had over a week to go before Jade came out the House, so this was to be a lengthy kidnap assignment. Our hotel location didn't stay secret for long. We smuggled Jackiey in through side doors and underground car parks, but the other papers found us and decided to join our party twenty-four hours later. On Day Two of the *Big Brother* stakeout, a man knocked on Jackiey's hotel room door brandishing a cheque and an open letter offering the earth. Unfortunately, they were met by the sight of a half-naked Crump who had swapped rooms with Jackiey – now sharing a twin room with me and under twenty-four-hour scrutiny. Crump sent them packing.

By Day Three, the paparazzi were outside and we'd heard whispers that journalists were applying for jobs as reception staff on the desk below. My paranoia was in full swing. 'Don't let anyone speak to her,' the News Editor had instructed that morning. 'She speaks to no one without written permission from The Editor.' That no speaking to her rule went for the Channel 4 bosses, too. They would ring me every few hours, growing increasingly furious as I forbade them to chat to my kidnappee.

'I'll get her to the House on Final night,' I promised. 'Until then, no one talks to her. No TV appearances. And I can't say where she is.' All very 007, but I guarded Jackiey with my life, snarling at probably perfectly innocent girls in hotel loos when they tried to say hello. No chance. They might be a rival hack after a quote. I batted all attempts away and, for five days solid I never left her side.

At 2.30 am one morning the fire alarm went off. Jackiey prepared to flee in her brand new silk pyjamas, before Crump burst open the door and screamed, 'Stay put!'

Fire alarms are another classic tabloid tactic. If there's ever anyone in a hotel who you want to talk to or photograph, you simply set off a fire alarm in the middle of the night and wait for them all to run outside. If they are secret lovers you simply wait outside their room and grab video footage as they both flee for the fire escape. If it's a chat you're after, simply sidle up to them as they gather outside in confusion, looking for the imaginary fire. All this is, of course, a terrible offence, and a complete waste of fire brigade time and resources. Should you ever do it, do check for CCTV cameras first.

Anyway, Jackiey was made to risk any flames and stay put. The alarm stopped and we went back to sleep.

As the week went on, our rivals got more and more desperate as it became clearer and clearer that the only story anyone wanted to read about *Big Brother* was Jade's. The tide had turned. From branding her a monster, the papers had now realised she was the nation's new sweetheart and started saying 'sorry'. Jade was the most wanted woman in Britain. And Jackiey, her sole, available representative outside the House, was the only way to get to her.

Jackiey continued to enjoy her captivity. We went for shopping trips round distant parts of London to escape detection. Private spa rooms were rented out, and Jade's mum was massaged, treated, cut and blow-dried. I had a friend who owned a top London restaurant and we smuggled her in via a fire escape one day into a private dining room. I'd told him it was a 'top secret celebrity' I needed 'VIP treatment' for and he popped by, hoping, I think, to meet Angelina Jolie at the very least. He was a bit surprised to meet me, Crump and a kidnapped lesbian attacking his wine cellar instead. We kept moving hotel rooms. We seriously considered buying a burkha at one point. Paranoia was rife. The News Editor hired a people carrier and taped black bin liners over all the back and side windows so no one could photograph or spot Jackiey in the back seat as we drove around town. An ill-conceived plan, if you ask me. I couldn't see a bloody thing through the back and we're lucky we didn't kill Jackiey en route to Harrods.

Rather brilliantly, Jackiey pointed out that every journalist and pap chasing us was male, and suggested a quick detour into an all-female spa she knew. We spent a highly entertaining couple of hours there wallowing in the Jacuzzi – giggling at the fact that the woman everyone wanted to photograph and talk to was running around a spa, swigging champagne as the foiled male hacks were forced to wait outside getting absolutely rat all for their efforts.

And each day, between shopping trips, we worked on writing the story of Jade and Jackiey. It was to be the first time it was told and it was a surprising one. Jackiey was unflinching. The most honest interviewee I've ever had. She outlined how she'd begged social services to take Jade away from her as a child, because she worried she'd harm her in a violent outburst. Jackiey was prone to frustrated bursts of fury, after breaking her neck and collarbone and paralysing one arm in a motorcycle accident. She'd hit Jade in rows. 'I beat her black and blue,' she told me tearfully one afternoon. 'I asked her to go on the risk list because I was terrified what I would do to her.'

I think I felt more guilty for what had been written about Jade with every minute. Jade had never once mentioned anything about her childhood in *Big Brother*. It became increasingly apparent that we had got Jade utterly wrong. We'd got Jackiey wrong, too. Jackiey was not a monster, she was a woman who was just fiercely protective of her daughter and ashamed of how she'd treated her in her early life. But wanted to make up for it now.

Mind you. I'm not saying Jackiey was a saint. In fact she was one of the naughtiest, most mischievous kidnappees I ever had. She chain-smoked spliffs, for a start, and I ended up paying out over £200 in bribes to hotel staff to fumigate rooms as we left. I would trail around after her spraying perfume to cover her cannabis trail, praying I wouldn't get barred from Selfridges and Harrods.

In the end, I decided the safest thing was to move her out of the hotel and into my own home. For the last two days of the kidnap, Jackiey sat merrily cross-legged on the floor, spliff in hand, eating old pizzas we found in my freezer, while Fleet Street searched for her in London's finest hotels. My home, I figured, would be the only place the hacks would never think of looking for her, and I was right. I used the tactic on several occasions after that, and was never discovered. My flatmates learned to expect the oddest events in the kitchen. I had a rather lovely one called Kath at this point, who worked in government. She'd made the mistake of leaving her jacket and coat in the living room during Jackiey's kidnapping. Apparently her explanation when she turned up at No.10 stinking of marijuana caused a few raised eyebrows amongst government officials. She moved out shortly afterwards.

Jade emerged from the House the following day, to an offer from every newspaper, magazine and TV station in the country. If you watch the footage of Jade coming out the House, you will see Jackiey go up to her and say in her ear that she has got her a deal. We watched the screen in the office and cheered when we saw it. Good girl! Jackiey spoke to Jade at length in the early hours and explained she'd had a rather fabulous week, and the next day Jade came to us. We'd won.

It wasn't just an act of gratitude. Jade was signed up by a top agent and was given an extremely handsome £250,000 for her chat – then the largest ever pay out in newspaper history. A hastily hired PR team flung their arms up in horror when they saw Jackiey's interview and desperately tried to edit the copy, wanting her to whitewash her past. Mother and daughter both refused. 'It's the truth. I want it in,' Jackiey and Jade both said. I admired them for that. The interview with her mother ran ahead with Jade's blessing, and the agreed amount we'd discussed all those days ago at the Bermondsey flat was paid. The next day Jade took up half the paper and the splash.

'Not a bad little haul,' I smirked at Robohack, who'd merely managed a top on page eighteen, despite his staff reporter status. Something about Rik Waller, I think. 'I think that's what you call a buy-up.'

So this was the start of Jade and her relationship with the press. And I genuinely believe Jade was one of the smartest women in showbiz. Certainly the most honest and accepting. She got the whole crazy system more than anyone else I ever interviewed during my time in the tabloids. She would answer any question. Laugh at any publicity stunt we asked her to do over the years. And she was always willing to work. I once interviewed her as she was going into labour.

Looking back, the media was unforgivably vile to her – both the TV programme that twice portrayed her as a hate figure, and we tabloids, who almost destroyed her in both her incarnations in the House. But she'd happily give interviews to all those who had attacked her, no matter what they had printed or said. 'It's just how the business goes,' she'd say. 'Journalists are just doing their job. There's no point bearing a grudge.'

I was no better than anyone else. After all, I kidnapped her mother, told the world of her childhood abuse, and would happily have done a kiss-and-tell on her if I'd been able to with her dog-brandishing ex. But I would get a hug and a cheery smile every time I saw her and that never changed, right up until her final months. 'What are they making you do now?' she'd cackle, as she saw me come up her drive to check yet another 'row' or 'heartbreak' or 'new man', or 'new breasts' or 'new baby' story over the years. Until finally, she was sitting in a TV studio, with months to live, doing her last ever story as she prepared to talk about her cancer. Still smiling though.

'What was she like?' I am often asked.

What was she like? Well, she was no saint, but I only saw a flash of her famed temper once. It was on that first day we met, the day after she left the *Big Brother* House for the first time. She was in a right strop in the studio whilst she posed for pictures for our £250,000. She was tired, she didn't like the dress the stylist had bought her. She wanted to wear her jeans.

I took her outside for a chat where she admitted the real reason for the tantrum was she was fed up that she didn't 'beat that bloody Kate Lawler' and 'didn't get the seventy grand.'

'Yeah. But we're paying you quarter of a million,' I pointed out.

'I know. A quarter. What's a quarter? Nothing. If I'd won I'd have got seventy grand,' she wailed.

I wrote out £70,000 on a piece of paper. Then I wrote out £250,000 and made her count the noughts. 'You've got more noughts,' I said. 'You've won.'

'Oh,' she said. 'Is quarter of a million more than seventy grand?'

'Yes it is,' I reassured her. 'A lot more.'

'Did Kate Lawler get quarter of a million?'

'No,' I told her.

'So I beat Kate Lawler then?'

'Yes,' I told her. 'You won because you got more noughts.'

'Bloody hell,' she said. 'Why didn't you say? I'd have got my tits out if I'd known.'

During Jade week I slept a total of ten hours in eight days. I lost half a stone in weight, was smoking forty cigarettes a day and at 8 pm on Saturday night, when it came time to hand over Jade and her mother to a another paper which had bought the second part of the buy-up, I couldn't talk, think or even sit upright any longer.

I got a cab to a friend's house, where I apparently arrived mid-garden party, mutely drank three bottles of wine and then fell asleep on the floor. I was put to bed, where I stayed until Monday night, forty-eight hours later, when I woke with a start. I had to be in the office in less than ten hours' time, at Conference, where I was bound to be getting a bollocking as I had no stories for the next edition. In journalism, you're only as good as your next story.

But I'd also won, thanks to Jade. I arrived in the office to hear I'd finally been made a full-time, fully-fledged staff reporter. Anne had a contract ready that said I'd finally done it. Finally, a commitment. We were going steady.

'Sign here,' she said. 'Sell your soul. They own you now.'

And we both laughed and pretended she was joking.

174

My parents were proud of me, when I rang back home with the news of my staff position. Although perhaps slightly perturbed that this mark of success inevitably meant that I would be staying in London and in newspapers for good. I'd been making the odd phone call back home in tears that year, and I think the hope was that one day I was going to see sense and stop all this tabloid nonsense.

But I wasn't going to stop now. I had only just started.

'Anyway, who's Crump?' my mum asked, hopefully.

'Oh,' I said. 'Not marriage material.'

'Oh,' she sighed. 'Never mind. Something will turn up.'

10

SEX, LIES AND SHOWBIZ

And the Art of Expenses

'I LOVE GAY PORN!! I LOVE GAY PORN!' flashed the computer screen at the back of the TV news bulletin.

A cheer went up from our newsdesk as they watched the screen. Crump was wheezing with laughter and had to be handed an inhaler. The whole office had gathered to watch a former colleague leap to the computer and start frantically trying to cover the screen with his hands. In the foreground of the news programme, the po-faced newscaster continued to read the headlines, oblivious to the flashing message blaring out from the glass screen behind him, or the man frantically tugging at his mouse and keyboard as his TV colleagues turned round to stare in disgust.

'Brilliant,' said Crump, wiping his nose and eyes and pumping medication into his throat. 'Just brilliant.'

A new email was currently doing the rounds. It arrived with an innocent looking attachment marked 'Urgent!' Click on that and your screen would go blank, before filling with bright pink flashing letters proclaiming your love of homosexual erotica. It was accompanied with a loud siren. It was very funny.

The only way to stop it was to pull the plug out the back of the computer. As the news bulletin finished on TV we could see the sweating form of the ex-colleague, who clearly still hadn't worked this out. The man had left the paper the week before, and today was his first ever shift at a TV newsroom. Judging by the looks he was getting, it was about to be his last.

He wasn't the first to have his day ruined either. Just hours before we'd also sent it over to the political editor in Whitehall. He emailed a very angry missive back, saying he'd just had a horrifically embarrassing incident in front of the Prime Minister and, in future, could we keep our puerile jokes to ourselves.

'Oh dear,' said Crump, turning away from the screen. 'That'll teach him to leave us for the fluffy world of TV. Right then,' he added, turning to me. 'Now, you got his staff position didn't you? Now you're staff, you get expenses. Happy days. Come on. Pub's open. I'll tell you how it all works.'

Things might have been shit on the personal front but my work life was finally looking up. I was about to learn one of the most important things in tabloid journalism. Expense accounts and how to abuse them. Incidentally, if you do ever find yourself in the position of filling out an expense form for a newspaper, I'd like to make it clear that the following could land you in very deep trouble with HM Revenue & Customs. I merely list all this as an example of what the worst amongst us were prepared to do.

Trainee journalism and shift working are pretty badly paid considering what you have to do on them. About £70 a day, after tax, on a national newspaper – which given that you could have been chased and sworn at by all manner of people that day, is not a lot. Rates have barely risen since the 1970s and nor will they, when there are so many people streaming out of media courses and desperate to get in. You get even less working at a news agency, or on local or regional papers.

Tabloid newspapers are a bugger to get into, bloody hard work and the pay is horrendous. And yet still people apply in their thousands. However, all this effort becomes worth it, financially speaking, once you hit a staff position. For now you not only – finally – get a decent wage, you get expenses too.

Expenses. Now this is something that journalists do very well. Once again, none of this was taught on my journalism course and it was all very definitely illegal. But when Crump took me aside on this first day of official staff reporterdom, he told me that one of the things you have to learn if you're going to survive in journalism is how to get a 'blanko'.

A blanko is a blank receipt – a highly prized acquisition for a hack. There's a whole industry devoted to it and Crump was to teach me some of the tricks over that highly lucrative (and receipted and, naturally, claimed back) pint. It's basically fraud. But highly creative, inventive fraud.

'We've got things we need to support,' said Crump. 'Habits. None of this is cheap. Let me tell you how the old blankos can help.

'First up,' he started, 'every cabbie is your friend. Most friendly black cab drivers in London can be persuaded to hand over a book of blank taxi receipts in exchange for a cash tip of around £50, on top of their fare. Fill these receipts out for a tenner a time, and, over the weeks, an experienced blanko handler can transform this into a good £700 on expenses. Even if you can't quite persuade them to give up a whole book, most cabbies will hand over at least a couple of blankos if you give them a fiver – a tip which then transforms into a straight 400 per cent profit when filling out those expenses forms later on.'

Blankos are a fairly widely used con in journalism. On an average morning – once the bosses were safely out of earshot in Conference – the office would be alive with the shouts of, 'Make that a ten, would you?' Or, 'Give me a twenty on that,' or 'What would you say the fare would have been from Wapping to Hampstead if I hadn't got the tube?' Assorted hacks would openly pass around blank taxi receipts for each other to fill out, thus ensuring that their multiple sets of receipts would all have differing handwriting on them. For added authenticity, we'd write them on our knees, shaking the seat to simulate an engine.

Once a month, a district reporter from a regional paper would arrive in the pub for lunch and a catch-up with a selection of staffers from the nationals. This was a profitable couple of hours all round. He'd turn up with local restaurant and bar receipts from around his area. 'I've got a Manchester, a Cheshire and a Didsbury,' he'd say. 'Any takers?' There would *always* be takers. These receipts were gems. The beauty was that they not only enabled you to claim you had 'met a contact' in an out-of-town area and needed reimbursing for the dinner and drinks you'd bought them, but – if you were being extra cunning – you could also claim back petrol by filling out a mileage allowance form saying you'd driven there and back. The district reporter would flog in a few stories that he'd actually picked up from the region, which you could then print up in the paper under your byline as 'evidence' of the fruits of this long old drive and lunch. And everybody was happy.

Crump was a master at expenses. I only realised to what extent during that buy-up with Jade, when Jackiey and I came hurtling out of the hotel one day and jumped in the back of the van as Crump sat in the front in the driver's seat.

'Drive, drive!' I screamed, probably in a completely over-the-top fashion, imagining us being in the centre of some movie chase-scene, with the paps in pursuit and the getaway car at the ready. Crump put his foot down. And bunny-hopped twice down the drive before crashing the gears and then almost smashing into a bollard.

'Crump?' I said, as he asked where reverse was. 'You can drive, can't you . . .?'

He hadn't set foot behind a steering wheel since passing his test twenty years ago, he admitted. He didn't even own a car. Which was odd, because I sat next to him at the time and had watched him claim at least £200 a month on 'petrol and mileage', plus hundreds more on 'valet fees' from 'couriering' pop stars.

It wasn't his only scam. Crump had a nice little backhander deal with a stationers in East London, who, when printing receipt books up for local restaurants, would spin off a few extra sheets for him and sneak them to him for a cash payment. He even had receipt books made up for his own, entirely imaginary London wine bar, which the stationers had designed receipts for. And then submitted multiple handwritten receipts saying he'd had lovely, if slightly expensive, nights out there with contacts.

Others went still further. One hack swore blind that the only way to expose one public figure's dodgy deeds was if he pretended to be a Lord. He duly spent a wonderful month living in a penthouse apartment in Mayfair, complete with a full-time manservant and a butler who would announce his Lordship's arrival into all the ballrooms he attended during the month. I can't remember if he ever got the story or not, but I can remember that half the newsroom went up there regularly to join his Lordship in drinking Krug on expenses.

Another particularly inventive hack even went so far as to enrol on a series of foreign language night-school classes. Any journalist returning from an overseas job would hand over a series of blank receipts to him, and, for a small backhander, he would fill these out in immaculate French, Italian or Spanish. There were rumours that one old-time journalist funded an entire extension to his house with a single overseas trip to Iceland.

And a particularly brilliant claim came from a foreign correspondent who was reporting from Somalia. He claimed he needed £700 wiring in cash, so he could buy a camel and reach his incredibly important interview subject. When this was queried by the Managing Editor, who demanded some sort of proof of this outrageous travelling expense, the correspondent responded two days later with a request for a further £500. Saying he needed it for a 'camel burial fee', as his beast had sadly just demised.

Immoral yes, but, we figured, our billionaire bosses could afford to stand us the odd dinner. Competitive expense claiming was an office sport and particularly good examples were celebrated. Besides, it sort of made up for all the years of impossible tasks, lousy wages and bollockings we'd had thrown at us.

Maybe it was all illegal. Immoral. Grasping behaviour. But it was funny. And we left a lot of happy restaurant owners and well-tipped cabbies in our wake. And at least we didn't claim for moats like the MPs, and we weren't ripping off the taxpayer. Mind you, I do have to laugh every time I see a thundering report from tabloid hacks slagging off 'Fat Cat expenses'. We tabloid cats were positively obese when it came to expense accounts. Ah, expenses. It's one of the things I missed most of all when I left.

Anyway, these sort of arrangements enabled us staffers to enjoy all-afternoon and sometimes all-night drinking sessions at the paper's expense and a generally comfortable lifestyle when not ensconced in the madness of the day job. Put down a celebrity's name and the receipt would be waved through no questions. Although, I did have a slightly tricky situation once when I was introduced at a launch to Sharon Osbourne. I gave my name and formally shook her hand. The newspaper executive with me raised his eyebrows questioningly. Because according to the expenses he'd been signing off, we'd been having raucous and highly expensive dinners together at The Ivy for years. 'She always blanks me at press do's. Doesn't want anyone to know she's my secret squirrel source,' I muttered, unconvincingly, as Mrs O passed by, with not a flicker of recognition.

Occasionally you'd get found out, hauled in, given a dressing down. But it was never a serious one. Even when Crump had tried to sneak in a set of golf clubs on a hotel bill – whilst on a job trying to rescue two pigs in Tamworth – he only got a mild ticking off from the desk. Likewise, when his phone bill arrived – which showed he'd also been calling 0898 chatlines on the company mobile one night to while away the late hours on a job – he got away with it. Said it was 'vital disarming work'. As long as you worked hard, kept filing, kept delivering, then the odd dodgy claim was accepted, a blind eye was often turned, and at the worst you'd get a slapped wrist and perhaps a football half-heartedly aimed at your head.

Expenses weren't the only good thing about being a staff reporter. Moving to Showbiz was a real improvement on the working day. Some people actually welcome you with open arms when you're a Showbiz journalist, rather than trying to attack you. Not all of them mind. But more of the grievous bodily harm threats later.

But anyway, I was just happy that my new staff position in the Department of Silly Stories meant I was finally out of the latex. And I think it was easier on my parents too. Our phone calls got longer anyway.

'I'm at the National TV Awards with Trevor McDonald,' I said on my next phone conversation back home to my mother, when she asked what I was, 'doing in newspapers' this week.

Next time it was, 'I'm just off to Simon Cowell's house.' That was an interesting afternoon's interviewing actually. He'd just become a massive success as TV's Mr Nasty on *Pop Idol* and was still at the stage of trusting journalists and inviting them into his home for interviews. I soon changed all that. Once inside his house I pretended to need the loo and had a good ten minutes left on my own, noseying around his downstairs bedroom and private bathroom.

What I was actually doing was following Crump's instructions. 'Try and find some hair dye,' he'd said before I left. 'I'm sure he's dyeing that barnet. It's a page lead if you can get some evidence.'

Cowell left me alone for ages in the bathroom. Perhaps his Hollywood contacts had passed on the news about my dodgy stomach, but I was left in there alone, long enough to scour every inch of his downstairs loo which was roughly the size of my flat. I checked every cupboard and drawer. No dye. Damn it.

Eventually, he came looking for me. Unfortunately by then I'd progressed into his bedroom, looking for more page leads. There I had opened a cupboard to find row upon row of identical jumpers and trousers stacked up inside. I was rummaging about in there when he came looking for me, and I have to say, he did take it very well when he came down to find me elbow-deep in his waist-high trousers.

'What you doing?' he asked. Very politely. He's always very charming, Mr Cowell. Everyone says that. Even to hacks who are going through his underpants.

He was also very charming, when, just months later, we ran a kiss-and-tell with a girl named Debbie Corrigan who claimed, 'Sleeping with Simon was like a P&O ferry. You roll on and then roll off again.' In reply, Cowell merely laughed, said it was a good story, he hoped she'd been paid well and that he didn't blame the paper for printing it. Which made us feel guilty, so the next time we made sure we had a couple of lap dancers who gave him an absolutely cracking write up.

Anyway, back to Sir Trev. It was so nice to be able to say I was out with a Sir for a change. So much better than, 'Hi, mum, I'm at an S&M party looking for a bloke off the telly to covertly film on my undercover camera, but I can't figure out which one he is because everyone's wearing gasmasks.' That's the sort of thing I'd been avoiding saying down the phone line to Lancashire before I'd switched departments.

'Ah, Trevor McDonald,' said my mum. 'I like him. And that Simon Cowell is doing well too. Is he single? Is he nice? How old is he? Did he have a nice kitchen?'

I think my family hoped I would settle down with someone nice off the telly. They would ring with ideas. 'Grandma likes that Mark Durden-Smith,' they'd say. 'Or what about that nice man from *Vets in Practice*? Or Ben Fogle. Is he there?' There was great excitement when I was due to interview Richard Branson.

I think perhaps they hoped I was gadding around the parties, elegantly sipping cocktails and sizing up eligible blokes from the telly. Sadly not. Although, thanks to work, I did end up with one under my duvet . . .

11

MY NIGHT OF
SHAMEFUL LUST

*And the Art of Getting too Close
to the Story*

I'll spare you the finer details of my torrid romp. Just because I worked on the tabloids, there's no need to go into tabloidian details about lust-fuelled shenanigans or wild nights of passion, with legs in whatever positions are fashionable with newspaper reporters these days. And I won't be posing in my knickers, thank you.

So let's just race through the events. Let's do the quickest of confessions. Let's skip through a press conference and a screening with the cast of a new drama production in attendance. Let's hurry past a five-hour red wine drinking session. With tequila chasers. Let's fast forward to someone – shortly after the hotel's bar manager gave up in despair and turned all the lights up and pleaded with us all to leave – someone suggesting we all went up to a hotel suite and carried on partying.

Let's brush over me demonstrating in the corner of the room that I could, indeed, do the splits – I think the conversation had veered onto ballet lessons at this point, as I remember someone else swinging a girl above his head. Let's draw the discreet veil that I later wished I'd been wearing during my *Folies Bergère* topless dancer rendition, which I seem to remember attracted lots of applause. And let's just kick things off at the point when I woke up in a highly expensive Egyptian cotton-sheeted king-sized bed, in the middle of Soho, looked at the pillow next to me and thought, 'Blimey. That's that bloke off the telly.'

I did a quick check to my left. No. No one else there. And one to the right. Still That Bloke Off The Telly; no sign of any other cast members. One quick peek under the duvet. No, it was definitely just us. And a naked us I see. So, I concluded, something interesting had probably just happened.

I lay there with a massive grin on my face. Brilliant. I thought. I've finally cracked it. I've pulled.

My phone went.

Two minutes later I put down the phone, formally introduced myself to That Bloke Off The Telly, and told him I had a bit of bad news.

The phone call had gone like this:

''Ere, you were at that launch thing last night, weren't you?' said the News Editor.

'Yes,' I answered. Trying to sound as much as possible like a woman who wasn't still there at the launch thing, still under a duvet, with one of the thing's launchees.

'Apparently [insert name of That Bloke Off The Telly] copped off with someone last night. Naughty boy, hey hey? His missus will not be happy.'

'His missus?!' I had squawked. Looking at That Bloke Off The Telly with disappointment. Oh, damn. My first celebrity boyfriend and he turned out to be married.

That Bloke – oh, let's just call him TBOTT for speed – TBOTT had just rolled over to look at me from his side of the duvet. Presumably, to see who it was doing all the squawking. He looked quite surprised to see me, too.

I waved. 'So where did you hear that?' I said again, into the phone signalling to TBOTT that I, 'wouldn't be a minute'.

'Oh, the barman at the hotel. Crump's a mate. Apparently everyone was in a right state last night. Get this, the little tart he took up there even rang down from the room and complained that the porn movies online weren't good enough, because she was friends with one of the cast and it was putting them off.'

I had vague, guilty flashbacks of making a phone call about Linsey Dawn McKenzie, who I'd previously interviewed.

'That's disgraceful,' I murmured.

'It's a biggie, this. I'm putting it at the top of The List,' the News Editor had said. 'What went on, then? Can you file some colour?'

I muttered something vague about being at the party early on, and then, as casually as possible, added, 'So . . . shall I handle this one, then? Shall I go back to the hotel where he's staying?'

'Nah. Crump's doing it. Like I said, he knows the bar staff. He's on his way over now. Apparently they're both still there.'

I hung up in a sweat. Told the by-now-really-quite-cross-looking TBOTT that, 'Sorry, this really is quite urgent, I'll explain in a bit,' and called Crump's mobile.

'Morning,' said Crump.

Oh, thank God. He didn't know. 'Listen, I sort of have a source on this job you're on. Shall I go over to the hotel and cover it for you?'

'Yeah, all right,' said Crump.

I winked at TBOTT. He glared back.

'Actually, tell you what,' added Crump down the phone.

'Yeah?' I said.

'Why don't you just put your clothes back on and come downstairs and join me? I'm in the bar.'

Oh, bugger.

The story was quietly dropped.

'Don't worry,' Crump had said to me over a reviving G&T. 'These things happen. You just got a bit too close to the story. You're not the first. I always look forward to the Soap Awards myself. Those *Hollyoaks* girls are *lovely*.'

Several years later, TBOTT is still married and still regularly interviewed about his wonderful life with his adoring wife and family.

I interviewed him about it all once myself.

'TBOTT? Oh yes, he was nice enough,' I told my parents later. 'Didn't really get a chance to chat much to be honest.

'The car's fine thanks,' I added.

'You don't have children of your own, do you?' stated a sixty-something woman in khaki shorts, who was sipping white

189

wine at a garden barbecue party I attended around this time. The years had passed in Showbiz and I was now in my early-thirties. The duvet remained empty.

'Sorry?' I responded distractedly, still watching with pride as a three-year-old ran about the lawn in the fully-to-scale pink silk Disney Princess Aurora outfit that I'd just bought her.

'I can tell,' said the woman, brushing vol-au-vent flakes from a passing grandchild with a lightly tanned and bejewelled hand. 'We can always tell the childless people by the presents they buy, can't we dear? You should get on with it.' And with that, she turned to her lightly tanned husband and brushed flakes from him too.

Princess Aurora leapt in the swimming pool. That marabou trim on her crown will never recover, I thought, as I watched her soggy ascent.

That afternoon, I began to wilt, too. These days, within minutes of arriving at social events, people apparently felt free to inform me that they'd had me instantly marked out as one of life's sexless losers, that I was knocking on a bit and that I would end up childless. It seemed that even my gift choices conveyed total failure on the reproductive front. A harsh blow to the ego. And I was supposed to smile politely and eat vol-au-vents with them.

I comfort ate E-numbers from the pile on the buffet, and downed the Pinot Grigio.

The worst thing was that she was right. TBOTT aside, it was all still a void man-wise. And I was getting worse. For by this stage I had gone past the Denial stage, straight through Bewilderment and had by now progressed firmly onto the Bitterness and Resentment stage.

In fact, there was one girl at work who had a World's Best Girlfriend Mug on her desk. I'd sometimes spend hours just glaring at her, wondering what she'd done to get a man who loved her enough to buy her love-declaring crockery?

I would glare at couples on the tube. Shoot daggers at women on buses who wore wedding rings. Particularly if they were fatter than me. Particularly if they were holding hands with a man who was remotely attractive. How had *she* done it? What was it about her that encouraged men to drop to their knees and propose? What had she said, or done, or worn, that had convinced him she was The One. Why her? *Why not me?*

If people kissed in front of me, I would feel a physical pain of despair. I would tut at couples in supermarkets. *Why are you kissing her? She only went to the frozen section for thirty seconds. How could you possibly have missed her?* I'd been single for years. I coped. No one missed me when I went looking for my Findus crispy pancakes.

Once I'd passed thirty, I suddenly realised that people's reaction to hearing that I was single was changing. Everyone was starting to look at me a bit strangely.

At wedding ceremonies, I'd be forced to sit alone, listening with burning cheeks, as the vicar went on about the, 'delight and tenderness of sexual union and joyful commitment to the end of their lives'.

It wasn't through choice that I was alone, I wanted to shout as the vicar started intoning that, 'No man can live alone'. Don't have a go at me! I was perfectly willing to put on a frock and make promises in front of my weeping parents. I *wanted* a smug mug to drink my coffee from. I wasn't doing it deliberately. I'd tried. I'd gone speed dating for Chrissakes. But whilst everyone else was going home to, 'a way of life made holy by God', I was doomed to spend nights hand-plucking my moustache hairs, alone.

My friends, the married ones, tried their best for me. They scoured their address books and tried to fix me up. At one excruciating dinner party, they invited the last unmarried thirty-something single male they knew. I was positioned in the centre of the table at dinner, with the man opposite me. Our noses pointing at each other like stud farm inhabitants. 'He's the last one we know,' they said afterwards, as he hailed a cab and left without my number.

It was like an alarm bell had gone off, telling everyone else when to find a life partner, but somehow I hadn't heard it. And now it was too late. In life's game of musical chairs, it appeared I was the last one standing when the music stopped; looking bewildered and searching round for a seat, any seat, and suddenly realising there was absolutely nothing left. Everything had been taken.

Whilst all around me had been a maelstrom of passion, my life was like the quiet bit at the centre of the hurricane. Slightly littered and bashed about. But, drunken dalliances with love-rat actors aside, empty.

It wasn't just that I didn't have kids. I was also the only one without a mortgage. Who didn't have a pension. Or an ISA. I was the only one who still lived with flatmates. I thought I'd progressed because I'd made it out of a bunk-bed. But then I'd pitch up at these events and realise I was way behind. Every other one of my friends had adoring, committed life partners, who they kissed goodnight and held each night. I just lived with random people I found in *Loot*.

As I inhaled wine that afternoon at the garden party, on my own, refusing to take the tiara off my head, I realised it was now not only the parents, it was their children who had started to look at me strangely.

I competed day after day on stories, hit deadlines each day, filed each day. So why was it, in life's deadline to find a partner, I had been completely unable to succeed?

Fuck me. I was a bit of misery guts, wasn't I? It's no wonder I couldn't get laid.

Still, at least I had my work to sustain and fulfil me.

Not really.

For now, with perfect timing, was the time when the interview subjects started threatening to kill me.

God, and I thought it was all going to be so much easier in Showbiz.

12

HAPPY, HAPPY, HAPPY TALK

And the Art of the Death Threat

'Celebrity death ring round,' announced the News Editor, when some actor fell off their perch one day. 'We need it fast,' he told me. 'So go for the usual. Go for the usual B's.'

'The usual B's?' I asked, confused.

'Babs, Biggins, Blair – Lionel not Tony – and a bonus Bully from *Bullseye*'s Bowen,' he said. 'They're the only ones that pick up their phones to the tabloid press.'

Before the days of Twitter, when any celebrity death leads to an outpouring of online tributes from celebs, we actually had to ring the celebrities for quotes. Look at any newspaper when a national treasure dies and you'll see the same old names there. Barbara Windsor, Christopher Biggins, Lionel Blair, Jim Bowen. Phone the showbiz old timers and you'd not only get a lovely quote commemorating their fellow celebrity's demise, but also a heart-warming tale of the time they worked together in panto. The old pros will pitch up at award ceremonies, smile nicely when approached by journalists bearing idiot questions, and, no matter what gets thrown at them, will play their part in the whole publicity system and simply soldier on.

Not everyone is always so happy to hear from us. I once had to spend some time with Lauren Harries – that spooky antiques expert kid that went on *Wogan* as a little boy called James, and then later changed sex to become a woman. She was very strange. She ended up our little chat by staring into my eyes and declaring, 'I'm going to come and kill you.' Which was a bit unfriendly, I thought. And a bit worrying, too. Especially when she started saying she'd killed her Uncle, too. (Incidentally, the killing-her-Uncle-bit was just a fanciful flight of imagination, it turned out. Pity. I thought I'd picked up quite a good page lead there for a moment. The wanting to kill me bit may well have been more true. She was doing a hairdressing course at the time so there were twelve pairs of scissors on the table.) Unfortunately for her, by this time I was battle-hardened by Paxman and Jackiey, so I was quite calm about the whole thing. I merely reverted to my Northern roots, stabbed my finger at her chest and informed her I'd 'fucking lamp her one' if she tried it. After a brief pause, she backed down. 'Well okay, I probably won't kill you then,' she said. 'Or at least I'll try not to.' Baby steps, we agreed. Baby steps.

Honestly, you'd never get that from Biggins. And she wasn't the last to threaten bodily harm.

*

'I've got a bit of a treat for you, a bit of a scandal, bit of a flyer, but I think it will work,' said the News Editor one day.

A phone call had come in, from a member of the public, with a 'hot tip'. It had come in on the number we printed in the paper for just such tips. All the calls to this number had to be taken, indulged with a polite chat and checked out. Even the ones that came in from complete nutters. I once wasted a whole month checking out one bloke's claims. He swore blind he'd dated Dannii Minogue, was extremely close with royalty and offered to dish the dirt on all manner of extremely famous people. He'd worn hand-stitched shirts and hired a limo for our meeting, rented out a hugely expensive flat, showed a raft of pictures of him draped round various A-listers and he had all the jewellery and red carpet passes that appeared to befit his status as a multi-millionaire. Actually, he was a complete conman. I only realised this when I saw him at the TV Quick Awards one year, speaking in a New York accent and claiming to be Oprah's manager. 'But you told me you were from East London,' I said plaintively as he swept past, ignoring me, following the cast of *Loose Women* into the VIP area.

He later got arrested for pretending to be a senior Scotland Yard officer and turned out to have 102 previous offences. It seemed he wasn't a millionaire playboy but the skint son of a decorator from Bexhill-on-Sea. He would have been a brilliant journalist. He was utterly fabulous at subterfuge. Every single tabloid in Fleet Street had at some point printed at least one of his claims and he had every desk convinced he was a top-level source of A-lister stories. Me too. I was half way through writing a book with him before we caught him out.

He wasn't the only chancer. We'd regularly get calls from people saying they had 'a massive story' and if we could just hand over £20,000 in cash in a dark alleyway somewhere, they'd come and tell us all about it. Those ones we'd hang up on. Various people phoned in claiming to have spent the night with someone. There were ways of checking this out. There was one ex-*EastEnders* star who used to only sleep with women who were over a G-cup in their bust region. As each young female voice came on the phone claiming they had a kiss-and-tell, we'd simply bark, 'bra size?' We knew we were safe to hang up if they came back with a mere 32C.

Girls used to ring up claiming they'd bedded Premiership footballers, and as 'evidence' could describe every detail of their house. So, we would point out, can anyone who's just read their 'at home' spread in *OK!*. The easiest way to check it out was to ask them to phone their famous 'lover' in our presence, with a tape recorder running. Most, at this stage, would admit they were faking the whole thing. One girl took it all a little further. She'd rung in claiming to have slept with a footballer, but didn't have his mobile number, much memory of the night, or a shred of evidence about the whole thing. Thinking she was a fake, I'd told her we couldn't run her tale without any evidence. She rang back the following week saying she'd managed his teammate this time, 'and I took photos of him in bed as he slept. Will that be enough?'

It's harder to say who behaved the worst sometimes – the women who kissed and told, or the men that gave them something to tell about. Or us for printing it. You couldn't blame some of the girls for wanting revenge and a cheque.

One footballer enticed a young girl back to his and was mid-passion when they'd been interrupted by a tooting of a horn outside. 'That,' he had said, to the confused and newly deflowered maiden in his bed, 'is your taxi. So if you would like to leave now, please. It will wait for a minute whilst you get dressed.'

I always rather admired the WAG who arrived in reception once and deposited a video camera marked for our attention. It contained footage of the dozens of girls that her footballing other half had secretly filmed himself in bed with, and she'd found stashed at the back of the wardrobe that morning. She didn't even want cash. 'He'll give me enough of that after you run it and I divorce him,' she said as she waved goodbye.

But back to the hot tip phone line. Every once in a while, just occasionally, it's a genuine one. Nicky Clarke's girlfriend called up shortly after we printed the story of his cheeky grapple abroad. The girlfriend invited me round for dinner. 'Why would you want a tabloid hack round?' I asked, confused. 'Is this going to be some sort of big confrontation, shouting thing?'

'No,' she replied. 'It's just that every time he cheats on me, he buys me jewellery to say sorry. You lot keep finding him out and I owe you a thank you.'

This case, this scandal, this flyer, started off as a fairly dull phoned-in tip. We'd had an anonymous call about Captain Sensible. Yes, him. He of the red beret and the Happy Happy Talk. Hardly a World Exclusive, but it might make a back of the book spread. It sounded like a kosher tip and would be worth checking out, said the News Editor. The Captain had, said our phone-based Deep Throat, taken a gym-slip lover. Given that he was knocking on a bit and not exactly a God in the looks department, The Editor wanted a 'Beauty and the Beast' type story – 'What the Hell is She Doing Going Out With Him?'.

No payment was sought from the tipster – which was unusual – but names and full descriptions were given before they abruptly hung up.

I was charged with finding out if it was true. And if so, two thousand words were required by 5 pm, containing choice phrases such as, 'gym-slip love affair', 'wrinkly' and 'not very sensible'.

'Get driving, chop, chop,' said the News Editor. 'I told The Editor you were on your way.'

I was in the car five minutes later, on my way to the Captain's front door. It wasn't that difficult to find out where to go. Tracking down people's addresses is easy and quick when you're on a newspaper. Everyone in the country who has registered to vote is listed on the electoral roll, and news-papers subscribe to an online version of this. You simply type in the person's name (funnily enough he's not listed under Sensible, Captain), press 'search' and up pops the address on screen. On this system you can also see where they used to live, and get a complete list of everybody who's ever lived with them. This is very handy for tracking down ex-lovers.

Anyway, in this case, just three minutes after the phone call came in, I was en route to the Captain's doorstep hoping for some Happy Talk about his love life.

Clearly record sales were not what they used to be – the Captain's home was a bit shabby, I thought as I arrived there an hour later. Didn't look like the home of punk, rebellion and The Damned. It looked like an entirely unremarkable house on an entirely unremarkable estate with a neat little lawn. The best bet on this one I decided, was to take the straightforward approach. Knock on the star's door, and ask if they wanted to 'tell their story'. Showbiz types, particularly ones whose star is on the wane, usually go by the 'no publicity is bad publicity' mantra, and are delighted to be in a paper. Taking a younger lover is hardly a crime, and, I supposed, the old Captain may be glad to remind people that he was still sailing.

I knocked. A pretty girl answered the door.

'Hi,' I tried, with my best I'm-Here-To-Help smile. 'Is the, uh, Captain in?'

'No,' she said. She did look like the description I'd been given of the lover though. Fresh-faced and innocent.

'Look,' I said, trying to look as trustworthy as possible, 'I'm from the papers. Obviously you've got a bit of a famous boyfriend. How do you fancy a sit-down chat with some lovely photos about your romance? We can pay,' I added. Taking care not to actually specify an amount. To be honest, it was worth a few hundred, tops. But I made the word 'pay' as drawn out and enticing as possible, so it sounded like thousands were on offer.

'Oh,' she said excitedly. 'Oh yes. I am dating him, yes.' She clearly loved her notoriety as the local celeb's girlfriend and was quite excited about the thought of going on a national scale.

Bingo, I thought. Story stood up. All you really need to write a story in a tabloid paper is one word. Take any story.

Say, there's a rumour that pop star X is cheating on his woman. Off we go to the pop star's door.

Like this:

Knock. 'Are you having an affair, Mr Popstar?'

Now, if he answers 'no' – just one word, 'no' – I could have got 1,000 words out of that.

Popstar X yesterday furiously denied love cheat claims. In an exclusive interview the fuming teen icon hit back saying: 'No! I am not having an affair!'

The pop favourite spoke out yesterday as he battled claims from our scurrilous rivals that his relationship is on the rocks. They claimed he was engaged in a torrid romp . . .

You get the idea.

If he says 'yes', even better – that's at least 2,000 words and the splash.

Popstar X last night sensationally admitted, 'I AM a love cheat.'

He broke down and told us 'Yes! I am having an affair.'

In a world exclusive . . . etc. etc.

Add in a comedy headline around one of their song titles and you're off.

Yes, okay, so our interviewee may not have uttered a single word of the quotes that are attributed to them, but it's seen as perfectly acceptable tabloidese to turn a one word denial/confirmation into a three page World Exclusive interview, simply by adjusting their grammar a touch. So, should you ever find yourself with an unwanted hack on the doorstep, the absolute best way to deal with them is to say 'no comment', or do what Paxo did and silently frogmarch them down your driveway.

However, our young heroine did not know any of this. So, instead, she'd confirmed the whole lot and I now had, technically, enough to write the spread. Happy Talk. Happy days.

'Let me go and call him,' she said.

Even better. Perhaps a nice little sit down with them smiling into the camera. 'Great,' I said and attempted to follow her in.

Tabloid journalists will always attempt to get in the house. On these doorstep jobs, once you're over the threshold, you're in. Brits are brilliantly polite and dither for ages before asking you to leave. Always ask for a cup of tea, which will buy you at least five minutes of interview time whilst they make it and you can then sit there, slowly sipping it and asking as many questions as possible for about another ten.

On later jobs, I was to learn that as a woman I had a massive advantage when it came to doorsteps. I could pretend to be pregnant. Faced with a door that looks like it's about to shut in your face, a nice technique is to push out your belly, clutch it winsomely and say with a grimace, 'God, I'm so embarrassed to ask. But I'm four months gone and I desperately, desperately, need a wee. Please may I come in?'

People always think pregnant women are helpless souls who need to be nurtured, looked after and sat down. They think they can't possibly leave them standing, shivering, with pleading eyes and crossed legs on a doorstep. Once safely on the way to the loo, you could, of course, get a little nosey around the 'love nest' as you accidentally open a wrong door or two and have a good look round 'trying to find the bathroom'. Take a couple of photos if you get the chance. And possibly play for time with a bit of dried toast and water if you can fake a heave of morning sickness. That could give you at least another six hundred words plus an added chance to gain their trust and talk them into a full story. There was one reporter with a wheat intolerance. She had a falafel sandwich before every doorstop, blew up like a balloon and was absolutely unbeatable.

In time I would learn to wear tops one size too small and breathe out. Okay, it was bad. But I wasn't the only one that did it. Some bewildered people would open their front door to up to five pregnant hacks in a day.

Sadly, on this occasion our damsel wasn't that stupid and was savvy enough not to let me follow her into the house. A shame. I had to content myself with a glimpse of corridor through the closing door, wondering if it was okay to describe a modest detached estate home with neutral walls as a, 'wild love den'.

'He's not answering,' she said when she arrived back a few minutes later. 'And I'm sorry, but I need to go. I need to be somewhere.'

'Can I give you a lift, perhaps?' I said, looking as trustworthy as possible.

'Okay,' she said. And inwardly I cheered again. I'd just been handed another 1,000 words. This was even better than the cup of tea and butterless toast stunt. With a couple of wrong turns and a slow down at every traffic light, I had a nice long chat in the offing.

So in she jumped, and, in girlish chatter, proceeded to excitedly spill every detail of her 'romance' en route. Handily, I had a tape recorder hidden in the glove compartment whirring away, picking up every word.

It was all going tremendously well. I was maintaining a nice steady driving speed of 15 mph, obeying every amber light and giving way to every cyclist. Then the Captain phoned. And from the shouting down the receiver – the shouting I could hear right over on the driver's side – he was making it fairly clear that he was unwilling to participate in the interview and neither should she. Presumably he'd figured out – and this really was quite sensible of him – that any coverage of their relationship would inevitably be going down the 'what on earth is *she* doing with that old has-been?' route.

The poor girl went white. She asked to get out of the car. The Captain had, it appeared, decided it was distinctly un-Sensible to allow a story to go ahead. Our interview was, sadly, terminated.

An hour later I was driving home when my phone rang. 'You fucking run a word of that fucking story and I will fucking break your fucking legs,' came a voice.

I wasn't overly familiar with the back catalogue of The Damned, but quickly came to realise it was their former lead songwriter on the phone. Captain Sensible himself. Which was odd, as I didn't remember handing over my number to anyone.

There were more expletives. More threats. The Captain was very, very cross indeed. 'I know where you fucking live!' he added. Maybe he had the Electoral Roll system online, too. And on he went with other threats – all pretty much sticking to the grievous bodily harm and being very cross theme.

The conversation, though short, was enough to leave me

hyperventilating in the car and needing to pull over to calm down. I rang the News Editor in a blind panic.

'That's not very Happy Talk is it?' he said, cheerfully, from the pub. 'All on tape, I trust?'

'No,' I said. No, oddly enough, when driving along at 70 mph and getting threats to break my appendages, I hadn't thought to hook the mobile up to a tape recorder and try and get another six hundred words out of it.

There was a sigh. Here was something else that hadn't been covered by my college course. When being threatened by celebrities – should it ever happen to you – you must, apparently, always think to switch a tape recorder on. You can then put the whole thing on a tape and make a fortune on telephone lines, inviting the readers to ring in and listen to their favourite stars in a strop at ten pence a minute.

'That would have been brilliant. Snappy Talk,' he sighed.

I rang Crump. He was no better. 'Oh, bloody hell. Never mind. Hopefully you'll get a death threat on tape next time. That's worth a splash. Especially if you can get pictures,' he counselled. 'Look, I've got to go. Liam Gallagher's just turned up. Sometimes you can get a page seven punch-up out of him.'

I carried on driving home, completely terrified I was going to find my flatmate fending off a raging old punk-rocker with a baseball bat and a vendetta. The house was empty and quiet. I sprinted inside, double bolted the doors and downed two bottles of wine in quick succession, as I stared out the window, scanning the bushes looking for red berets. Alone in the house, I drank and drank, before deciding that the best thing to do was ring my parents at 1 am to explain that

Captain Sensible was going to kill me and what did they think I should do about it?

What should I do? Here I was, trying to act like a professional, making my way in the big old world . . . but clearly I wasn't doing terribly well. I knew, more than anything, they just wanted me to come back home.

The story never ran. Captain Sensible, the desk decided, was dispensable after all. It was spiked. For once, the lack of a byline came as a bloody relief.

That night I had desperately wished my flatmate would come home. It was the only night in a year that I felt that way. For I'd just started living with the Flatmate From Hell.

I'd moved out of the House of Spliffs by now, and had ended up in a flat-share. The nice political one had left, a couple of others had passed through over the months and now I was living with a woman who'd responded to my ad on the internet, requesting a flatmate who was 'a non-serial killer who perhaps occasionally washed up'.

The woman who answered laughed over the phone, saying she hadn't killed anybody. She looked round, admired a red velvet chaise longue I'd just bought to adorn the living room and then signed a contract saying she'd move in.

Big mistake.

Never, *ever*, move into a flat with anyone who is thinner and younger than you. The Flatmate turned out to be one of those women with neat buttocks and a perfect turny-up nose, who had a constant stream of men turning up begging her to marry them.

I hated her. I would will her to put on weight and would

spike her morning coffees with full-fat milk. Sadly, her buttocks didn't move, and neither did she. Her bed did though,
nightly, with yet another adoring boyfriend.

It was like living on the *Love Boat* that year. She'd hold
Nigella evenings for new lovers. She'd float about the flat in
silken pyjamas, cooking Christmas recipes even though it was
not yet winter. She would giggle into her latest boyfriend's
face as they spooned recipes stuffed with pomegranate into
each other's mouths, whilst I sat sulking, watching *Corrie* and
examining the scabs on my knees from where I'd fallen over
outside the pub the night before. They would mouth 'sorry' as
they emerged in towels from the bedroom to snuggle up and
watch *Masterchef* together, whilst I drank SlimFast on my
own.

I remember one bitter row. It was over the chaise longue.
I'd asked her not to romp on it (see, I can't help the
tabloidese) because it was the first piece of furniture I'd ever
bought. I really, really wanted to 'christen it' I'd said, to have
a wild night of lust on the velvet, and had been working
steadily on a local gym instructor. I'd lied through my teeth
to him and said I was a dance teacher; I was spending £40
a hour on agonising personal training sessions, trying to lure
him to my furnishings.

One summer evening, after yet another fruitless gym session, I arrived home with stiff thighs to find dishevelled
underwear and Fortnum & Mason chocolate wrappers on the
red velvet. As I hammered on her bedroom door in questioning protest, a male snigger confirmed my worst fears.

Enough, I thought, as I stared at the sullied velvet, was
enough. Four weeks later, I sought revenge.

'I need the bathroom,' I demanded that morning, when I caught the pair of them, giggling, on the landing outside the shower. They were wearing matching towels, holding hands and no doubt heading for some fun with the sensuous massage oil which I noticed had appeared in the bathroom the night before.

But today, I stopped them. I held out my towel to impede their passage and raised my voice authoritatively.

'I need the bathroom,' I said. 'Now.

'Because I'm going out on a date with The Hoff.'

13

HOW I HASSLED
THE HOFF

And the Art of Celebrity Dating

The one extremely positive thing about working for a national newspaper is that you can officially use the might of the paper to help your love life.

And it was during this period of my life that I decided the job could damn well start helping out with things in the duvet department. I was thirty-three and it was about time I got on with it.

So, I sat down at my keyboard one day and summoned The Hoff.

David Hasselhoff probably didn't realise he was going out on a date with me that day. I doubt if he actually knows we've had a date, actually. But I remember every second.

I was a Hoffette. Had been for three decades. I loved The

Hoff. Back on my bedroom wall in Lancashire, he'd lived for three years in prime position, where I could see him at night as I lay on my love-heart feather pillows. He was ten across from George Michael and six love hearts above Phillip Schofield.

This was in the days of his Michael 'Knight Rider' Knight incarnation, and I'd snogged old Michael's mouth so often it was worn down to a pulp, revealing the wallpaper beneath. I'd sometimes send myself cross-eyed, staring at him for hours.

As time passed and The Hoff's hair thinned out, my love had dimmed but not entirely abated. At least once a month someone would forward me a Hoff-related email invariably featuring The Hoff in his *Baywatch* shorts and perhaps holding a small kitten, smiling winningly and saying in a speech bubble, 'Don't worry. The Hoff loves you.'

And I loved him.

I even took a Hoff-related detour once, whilst on holiday in LA. I specifically drove out to Santa Monica beach to see if the lifeguards really do wear red shorts. Took me two hours to get there, all on the wrong side of the road. They do. And they blew their whistles at me when I went in the sea. Don't bother holidaying out there though. It's awful. The shorts are all okay, but I was the only one with less than a DD cup, no one drinks and you're expected to get up at 6 am and jog.

Anyway. Back to The Hoff. Even pictures of him disgracing himself at airports and rolling around drunk on the floor eating hamburgers were no barrier to my decades of desire. They just proved we had a lot in common.

Now, one of the advantages of Showbiz journalism is that you can force famous people who you fancy to spend time with you, simply by pretending you are interviewing them.

And it was thus that our date emerged. The Hoff had popped over to the UK to publicise some internet thing or other. I forget what, I didn't bother reading the press release, or listen to a word the earnest PR had said on the phone about high-speed ISDN connections. I only heard the 'would you be interested in interviewing David Hasselhoff?' bit. And I certainly I remember that I said 'yes'.

Everyone pulls the interviewing-people-you-really-fancy trick. And everybody then tries their luck during their one-on-one time with their fantasy figure. A bloke from one tabloid paper, whose looks meant he was ignored in most normal situations, had managed to bag Sarah Harding from Girls Aloud, a feat which impressed the newsdesk so much they gave him a whole showbiz column as a reward. One tabloid hack actually managed to marry Sinead O'Connor. We all really aspired to Jane Goldman, who'd bagged Jonathan Ross when she'd been working at the *Daily Star*.

In the entire ten years I worked on the papers, I never once managed anything quite so impressive. Although it wasn't for lack of trying. I once booked Martin Kemp in for an interview about *EastEnders*, although all I actually managed to do was sit on his knee, drooling and ask him to sing *Gold* (he declined). Still, at least I managed to touch him.

I also had a fruitless afternoon staring at Jason Orange from Take That, pretending to be interested in his acting role in a Lynda La Plante drama. If we're honest, it was a performance that was never likely to trouble the Bafta nomination com-mittee, but I looked earnestly into his eyes, debated his 'method' and suggested his was a performance to rival Sir John Gielgud. Sadly all I got to stroke was his ego. And there is actual photographic evidence of me manhandling Morten Harket, the lead singer from A-ha (he'd been just along from Pip Schofield on the love hearts display). I pitched up at a gig in Guildford, claimed I was there to 'do a very important interview', flashed my press pass and got into his dressing room. There, whilst stroking him gently on the elbows, I told Morten he'd been 'on my bedroom wall for years', and then tried to snog him when he asked if there was 'anything else' I wanted after my 'interview'. Shortly afterwards, I was forcibly removed by his PR and ended up being named on the band's official European website two days later. There was an article quoting A-ha's management which claimed that I had 'attaqué Morten', and quoted me as saying, 'Je l'aime, je l'aime'. It also has a reference to me, 'touchant le derrière'. My GCSE French mercifully prevented me from understand-ing the full details of the piece, but I suspect my conduct was seen as less than professional.

Still, I have some lovely photos from it in which, from cer-tain angles, I think we look like a couple.

Anyway, back to The Hoffmeister, who was over in the UK for a week. And to an email which arrived suggesting I, 'hook up with him when he's in town next week. Let me know if you're free, maybe Wednesday evening?'

'Hook up?' That was a bona fide guaranteed meeting. A date. 'Yes,' I told them. Thinking I'd probably end up named and shamed on another website, but what the heck.

'We don't want a piece on the internet,' pointed out Crump.

'Can I go anyway?' I said. 'Please? I just want to go and meet The Hoff.'

'Fair enough,' said Crump, who was proving to be an entirely excellent sort of boss. He pointed out that he was busy emailing Kelly Brook's lot for pretty much the same reason. 'Just make sure you do that spread on Darius before you go.'

People wonder why Kelly attracts quite so many acres of newsprint for every new job that she takes, when, if we're being brutally honest, she isn't exactly one of our most talented presenters. It's largely because male journalists are doing their best to cop off with her and therefore keep asking to interview her. The fact there is a ready supply of photographs of her in her knickers helps things get a nod from The Editor too.

But anyway, Crump's attempts on this occasion were to be, sadly, less than fruitful. But still, we lived in hope.

And so my Hoff Day began.

My Hoff Day was to last twelve hours in all. He was appearing first thing in the morning on ITV1's *This Morning*, where I'd started pitching up sometimes to comment on showbiz stories in the newspapers. (Okay, yes, that too was just an attempt to meet up with Pip Schofield – but it all turned out quite well and I've been going in ever since.)

So I'd meet The Hoff there, before my 'official', or 'Hoffical', interview date that evening. Great, I decided. So that's a date in the morning, and another one in the evening too. A second date. With luck, we'd be going steady by 8 pm. And the good news was that whilst he hated tabloid hacks and that may prove a little difficult at first, he apparently loved women on the telly. He'd already tried to cop off with Jenni Falconer the previous morning when he appeared on *GMTV*. I was, I thought, in with a chance.

So, it was all good. And I awoke the next day in a fine mood. Even when I had to knock to enter my kitchen because my flatmate was kissing some man up against the door. And then knock to enter the fridge, when they moved, entwined and in love, onto that. I stayed cheerful, resolute, happy for their young love, because I too was on my way to meet the man of my dreams. It was only when they attempted to snog their way into the bathroom that I felt the need to intervene and had barred the way, explaining that my need this morning was greater than theirs.

That's when I let the, 'I've got a date with The Hoff' boast drop. They stopped kissing and stared at me.

'It's this morning. And I'm seeing him again tonight too,' I told the disbelieving pair, as I swept in with a towel and some Veet. 'Keep the chaise free.'

When I arrived at the TV studios I flashed my identity pass and I got word – The Hoff was in the building. And The Hoff was in make-up.

I should have left him there. I should have been grown-up about it. I should have been professional. Maybe just waited until we were both in the studio, then shaken hands, told him I was also, 'in the TV business' (just like Jenni Falconer, hey?) and 'I believe my people called your people and we're meeting tonight?'. Not mentioning anything about the being-interviewed-for-a-tabloid-newspaper bit, obviously. I should have waited until the Hofficial date. But no. I couldn't wait. I marched straight into make-up screaming 'The Hoff's here!' to everyone I met on the way.

'Hey!' said The Hoff when I got there. He was sitting having powder applied to The Hoff brows, a pink make-up gown catching any spillages over his Hoff personage. He looked absolutely gorgeous.

'Hey!' I responded. The make-up room fell quiet. All heads turned to me. 'Hey!' I added again. Thinking my mum would love it if I hooked a Hollywood star. 'Hey,' I added, into the silence.

More silence. I had to think quickly.

Three bloody decades of preparation for this moment and I came out with, 'Would you like a cup of tea?'

A silence.

'Or coffee?'

'Hey, I'd *love* a cup of coffee,' said The Hoff. 'Black coffee with Canderel.'

'Black coffee with Canderel. For the Hoffee *loves* the coffee,' I reported breathlessly in the Green Room seconds later. 'A caffeinated Hoff is a happy Hoff.' One coffee was produced. Unfortunately it was produced in the only remaining mug – which happened to feature the Crazy Frog.

'Hey, I *love* Crazy Frog,' said The Hoff, back in make-up. I smiled.

'Me too,' I said. Making a Crazy Frog noise as I whisked the mug into his hand.

'We are getting on *brilliantly*,' I texted my flatmate.

We got on brilliantly all morning. He went on the show, did his interview bit, brilliantly, then did a showbiz walk along the corridors of ITV. Small children were held up to him to kiss. Grown women emerged from corridors to touch him as he passed. 'Hey!' he greeted them all. The Hoff loves you! Oh! I thought. He didn't even need a kitten. He really is perfect.

I trailed in his wake, smiling indulgently at the fans to show that I would never be jealous of them when he was mine. I was holding one of his shirts. I had offered to iron it for him after I took the coffee. 'Hey! I'd love that,' he had said. Okay, my interview wasn't textbook so far. I hadn't exactly asked him if 'anything unusual' had happened on the internet or mentioned anything about us being TV equals. I'd just taken his laundry requirements. But I had hours yet, and at least I'd demonstrated I had a caring, nurturing side and could do nice creases in laundry. I'd ironed the denim dreamily, imagining how one day I would do this every day. 'Am ironing one of David's shirts,' I'd texted my flatmate.

Women and babies were kissed and anointed with a Hoff wave. I passed with his intimate entourage of four into the lift, still clutching his shirt lovingly. Ignoring the fact I was due on live telly in about ten minutes. It could wait. I couldn't leave The Hoff now. I wanted to enjoy every Hoff-filled second. Surely, I thought, as I breathed in the presence of The Hoff, surely it wouldn't be long before I clutched The Hoff to my bosom adoringly, too. That night perhaps?

I loved him, I thought, as he shot a final 'Hey!' to the crowd of waving fans outside. I'm so over Matt LeBlanc.

As the lift doors shut, I sighed. Now, it was just me, The

Hoff and his inner entourage. A private glimpse of a great man. I looked up, sighed and prepared to say something really intelligent about *America's Got Talent*.

Then he did it.

He grolleyed up.

To be precise, he snorted up a bucket-load of phlegm from the back of his throat. Hacked it up in fact. And then swallowed.

'Hey!' I thought.

And he didn't even apologise.

In fact, he did it again. He stood there, hacked up lumps and smashed into my dreams. I watched in horror as he cleared his nostrils.

'I went to Santa Monica for you,' I thought, as a part of me died.

The lift doors opened, another crowd waited outside, waving. More babies were held aloft. The catarrh-free Hoff smiled and went off to meet his public. 'Hey!' he said to his public.

I stayed behind. Clutching the shirt. The scales fell from my eyes. Two decades. Two decades I had watched this man. Adored him. Downloaded him. Passed round pictures on email of him clutching puppies. And he'd just harrumphed up a throat-load of mucus without a second's consideration.

As I stared with newly opened eyes, I realised he was wearing mirrored sunglasses. That he had another pair of sunglasses around his neck. On a plastic string. His shirt, I realised as I looked at it in horror, was actually a bit naff. The man, I now saw, was in fact wearing a pale denim pants and shirt combo.

Twenty years. Twenty years of my life for mucus and two-toned denim.

'Okay, it's Milton Keynes next,' snapped a member of his entourage, hustling him out the lift towards a people carrier. 'It's a ninety, that's nine zero, minute drive. Does anyone need a comfort break?'

The mucus was not even mentioned.

I passed his ironed shirt over to her, gave a hollow smile and silently gestured that I was staying put in the lift and returning to the bright lights of Schofield and *This Morning*.

I cancelled the date by email that afternoon. 'Really?' said the PR. 'Really? Do you want the press release on the internet stuff?'

'No,' I said. 'It's over.'

'The Hoff had a coff?' asked Crump. 'Ah, never mind. Never meet your idols. Except Johnny Rotten that is. He was *brilliant* when I met him. I ended up on a twenty-four hour session with him and I woke up in a strange hotel room clutching a blow-up doll. Still got the photo somewhere. You must have had an off day when he was on about the koala bears.

'Here, Posh has had her tits done again. Write about that instead, we'll get a spread. Come on. Make it fast. The pub's open in ten.'

The good news is that I did finally pull around this time. I actually managed to have a relationship. The bad news was that it was with somebody completely unsuitable and I still couldn't tell my parents.

I underwent something of a dating renaissance as I

approached my mid-thirties. If you should ever find yourself in the position of being a desperate woman hurtling towards forty with a highly unsuitable job, then I have some advice for you. Go young. Go toy boy. Go for the ones that are too young to fully grasp your horrific life and just appreciate anyone who is willing to sleep with them.

You see, love – even for women who do not work on national newspapers kidnapping people and annoying celebrities – is tough once you pass thirty. In your teens there are men aplenty. You are practically flooded with men in their mid-thirties, begging to spend all their money on you and take you out in nice cars, and nice men in their twenties looking for The One. Aged eighteen, I'd dated a marketing director. Years after I ended it, my grandparents would still remind me that I'd been a fool to let him get away. 'Now that's the sort of man you should have married,' they said. 'A director. What's he doing now? Can't you ring him?'

Even in your early twenties, there are plenty of men. You get the new divorcees in their forties hitting on you, they're all delighted to have someone decades younger on their arm that they can shower gifts on and take to nice restaurants. Men in their fifties will have a crack, too. And although they all seem a bit on the ancient side when you're a youngster, you can usually get some nice jewellery out of them in exchange for agreeing to a dinner date.

And you think it's all going to last forever. All this men throwing themselves at you stuff. But hit your late-twenties and suddenly all the men disappear. I don't think it was just entirely down to my screwed-up job that this happened. A lot of women who have nice normal office jobs say the same.

And if you're still single in your thirties, you definitely hit problems. All the men your age and over are too busy dating thin teenagers to be bothered with you. They want the girls who are decades away from bothering them with awkward questions about their ovaries and marriage. Suddenly, there's a void.

The good news is, all you have to do is hang on for a few more years and you are, it appears, suddenly irresistible to toy boys.

Suddenly teenagers started becoming besotted with me. I noticed the post boy was gazing at me, all dreamy eyed. The work-experience kid slipped me his number. I had turned into a MILF. Without the M bit.

I think, to be honest, a lot of it is down to being easy. All the girl teenagers play hard to get, and need three months of meals and holding hands before you even get to first base and when you're on a student budget this just isn't practical. We (M)ILFs are up for anything after a bar snack. It's also down to bed sheets and breakfast. These young men all tend to sleep in scratchy bunk-beds in student dorms, and know that if they get a slightly desperate woman aged thirty-plus, they're not only in for Egyptian cotton, they'll probably get a cooked breakfast. If they're lucky, the old bird will be so grateful she'll cook you a Sunday roast too.

Whatever, after what had definitely been a bit of a lull, I wasn't complaining and launched myself into my Cougar phase with joy.

The post boy did stop by. To the amusement of the office, who would shout Special Delivery as the poor man made his rounds in the morning. And I dated a lovely IT engineer for a bit – although I had to call a halt to it when I went to visit him for dinner and realised he not only lived with his mum, he shared a bedroom with his brother. There was a brief flirtation with a male dancer, and I'd proudly show shots of him round the office, jumping about dressed as a swan, before I got ditched for a cygnet.

But I was still on a roll, and so, finally, came the teenage Egyptian Love God.

Ah, now he was a holiday romance. Holiday romances are ideal pickings for Cougars. A five-star hotel and room-service makes you a young man magnet. And this one was ideal. Not only was he young enough to enjoy my (M)ILF status, language barriers meant he couldn't quite grasp what I did for a living and, after a couple of hours trying to explain, we'd settled on the much more romantic sounding job description of 'writer'.

Yes, that was a glorious holiday in the Red Sea. I wrote postcards home saying the weather was fabulous, but to be honest I spent more time looking at ceilings than sky. And when I wrote about the view, I meant of the Love God.

The Love God worked as a diving instructor. His rippling muscles looked great in a wetsuit. When he was hoisting air tanks onto boats and giving team talks about dodging piranhas in the Red Sea, we'd all, all the holidaymakers on the diving trip, hung on his every manly word. I'd hung onto a bit more by day three, fuelled by lust, an all-inclusive hotel bar, and the knowledge that as I'd gone on holiday on my own, I could be as slutty as I liked and nobody would ever find out about it. Not having to get up and kidnap anyone made for a wonderfully relaxing lifestyle.

Anyway, I ended the two weeks with a smile on my face, an exchange of addresses, and a rather cute gold necklace with a 'Y' on it (for the first letter of his name) which I swore I'd wear 'forever'. Indeed, I did wear it all the plane journey home. Where, after boastfully showing photos of him in a wetsuit to my flatmate, I promptly forgot all about him. And what the rest of the letters were after 'y'.

Forgot, that is, until a month later when a nineteen-year-old boy turned up on my doorstep holding a suitcase. Wearing corduroy elastic-waisted pants, a nylon shirt and a hopeful expression. I began to regret that last minute exchange of addresses. All I'd really wanted was a Valentine's Day card. Not a personal appearance.

My flatmate had raised an eyebrow. 'Someone outside. Says he knows you,' she'd said, and watched as the small child hurled himself into my incredibly surprised arms.

Holiday romances do not really translate. Now he was no longer bathed in the Egyptian sun, and a rubber wetsuit, the sun-kissed God of the waves had lost a little of his lustre. The static from his shirt almost floored me. He announced cheerfully that he had a friend who could give him a job packing bags in a store, that he'd gained a student visa and that now we could 'really be together'.

Great, I thought. Contemplating the corduroy. And realising, on reflection, that it had been the whole fearless-in-the-face-of-piranhas and wetsuit thing that had made the package work for me on holiday. But still, the chaise wasn't doing anything else at this point, so I invited him in and quickly went in search of the necklace.

Now, my view on age-gap relationships is that they *can*

work – but women should never try one unless they're pushing at least sixty. Think Barbara Windsor and Joan Collins.
They get it right with their toy boys. Look at their arm and
you see a handsome eligible man there. Your immediate reaction is, 'Lucky woman. Good on her.' But I did all this when
I was approaching my mid-thirties, which meant I had a teenager on my arm. Which looked sort of wrong. Very Captain
Sensible-ish.

Still, I braved it out for a few weeks. I bought him new
trousers of a suitable hue and fibre. I went to visit him at work,
where he wore a green tabard and a name badge. I met his new
student friends and tried to overlook the fact I had knickers
older than some of them, and that I was the only one whose
life appeared to not be dictated by a lesson timetable. I tried
not to hit anyone when they referred to Madonna as 'granny'.

It was all going okay. It was sort of working out, bar a bit of
sniggering and my friends asking him if he needed any help
with his homework when they met him. I'd been passing
round the pics of him in his wetsuit in the office and smugly
referring to him as 'my boyfriend the diving instructor'. It
sounded so much better than part-time supermarket shelf-
stacker.

In fact, it was all going so okay that I might have continued, until he suggested 'going to a rave' one weekend. 'A
rave?' I had repeated, incredulously. 'A rave? What time does
it finish?' I asked, as his friends sniggered.

I'd never been to a rave. I was well over thirty. I didn't
know what you were meant to do at them. 'What sort of
music do they play anyway?' I tried. 'Do they do A-ha?' I had
offered as a (sort of) joke.

'A-ha?' his mates had asked, looking confused. 'Who the hell are A-ha?'.

The elasticated pants I could fix. The shelf thing I could overlook. But the A-ha issue made me realise I was too old.

This isn't going to work, I told him. I needed my sleep. I can't go to raves with teenage lovers, because if I don't have at least eight hours in a decent bed with a decent mattress in a nice quiet darkened room, I'll never make it through the horror of the daylight hours. Because on that side, things were getting worse.

14

BRINGING FLYERS TO LAND

And the Art of Making it Up

Wm e had a memo come round the office one day. It said that we were banned from having a kettle on the premises. Health and Safety had decided it was unsafe. We couldn't be trusted with one.

It always struck me as odd that millions of people trust what newspapers say. They trust us when we bring down governments. They trust us when we wreck careers. They trust us to influence world events at presidential level. Yet the people who actually employed us didn't even trust us with hot water.

Mind you. That's probably because they knew what we were really like.

People often ask if tabloid hacks make it up.

And the answer, I have to admit, is yes. Sometimes we do. Let me explain the system. I'll start with quotes.

Despite all you've heard so far, I wouldn't blame you for clinging on to an old-fashioned, quaint belief that quotes are gained after a nice sit-down chat with an interview subject, carefully taped, transcribed and written up. This is not always so.

Sometimes the quotes were written before we ever left the office. Before we even knew who we were interviewing. On one occasion, The Editor arrived at my desk and barked that an advert was to start running 'the next day', saying the newspaper had a 'brilliant' kiss-and-tell about someone from the pop group Steps, who'd just had a worldwide hit with the hideous song '5,6,7,8'. The kiss-and-tell was to run under the headline *My 5,6,7,8, Times Every Night with Steps Girl.* 'Great,' I said. 'Great story. Who got that then?'

'You did,' he replied. 'Or at least you better had get it by tonight. Find me someone to agree to that headline, or don't bother coming back into the office.'

Thankfully, after a seven-hour drive to Rhyl, a quick dash through the pubs, and a backhander of £100 to the local newspaper editor, a man called Andy emerged from the woodwork. He was an ex of the one called Lisa, and willing to agree to the quote for a lucrative sum of cash.

Sometimes, a combination of alcohol and cash did it. Like the time I was forced to spend the Millennium New Year's Eve, the turn of the century, the most momentous calendar date I would witness in my entire lifetime, on a Club 18–30 holiday. On my own. Up to my neck in other people's vomit.

I was, I think, from memory, there to do a searing investigation into the 'undercover story of the sordid drugs and sex
romps of shameless Brits abroad'. It was another brilliant idea
of The Editor's, I remember that much. In reality, I ended up
standing in a bleach-stinking hotel in the early hours of the
Year 2000, realising that everyone was far too drunk to be
doing any sex romps that day, and announced to the teenage
drunks in the bar that I would give £50 cash to anyone who
was prepared to say they'd had a fivesome and be photographed in a family newspaper. A collection of spotty,
drunken virgins from Harrow happily signed on the line and
posed, smiling and with thumbs up, for pictures.

So that's two ways of getting quotes. There are others.

Even when you see an interview with the celebrity themselves, together with a full set of quotes and big old smiley
picture, it's no guarantee that the whole thing hasn't been
entirely made up. In our defence, that's because the problem
with a lot of celebrities is that not many of them are that
bright. Being on TV or in a pop band makes a lot of celebs
think their IQ has automatically been raised, just because
people suddenly want to listen to what they've got to say,
print it or put it on the telly. But the reality is that, left to their
own devices, a lot of them just come out with utter tosh. But
this isn't an insurmountable problem. We can get round it.
We quite often just simply bypass the 'being interviewed'
stage.

What sometimes happened is this. The Editor decides they
want a celeb in the paper. He demands a lengthy interview on
a particular topic. With particular quotes. The journalist
realises that the celebrity is unlikely to come up with any of

this if they are actually spoken to. So the journalist then goes away and writes what would be the dream interview, with lots of dream quotes, then emails it off to the celebrity's manager with a message saying, 'is it all right if we print this, then?'. The manager then reads it and says, 'okay' and then in to the paper it goes. This works out well for all involved. The star gets some good press, the paper gets a good interview and the star doesn't have to go to all the bother and time of actually doing any work. Indeed, we can make them look really clever in the final edit if we need to. One Page Three girl did quite a nice chat about the Big Bang theory once. It's good business all round.

I did feel the odd twinge of guilt though. I remember once watching Jodie Marsh sob on *Celebrity Big Brother*, as she recalled a piece Jordan had 'written' about her in a paper. Jodie had declared war on Jordan with a bitchy article, and she sobbed on screen that Jordan had responded with a page-long annihilation of her glamour rival, saying Jodie had 'breasts like a spaniel's ears' and a 'nose like a builder's elbow'. That all sounds a bit familiar, I thought, as I looked back through my cuts.

Of course, Jordan had never said any of it. What had actually happened was that The Editor had arrived at my desk at 5 pm, told me he needed 1,000 words on Jodie that, 'sounded like they'd been written by Jordan' and that he wanted them overnight. So I'd gone home, drunk two bottles of white wine to bring out my inner glamour-model bitch and written a stream of complete bile. This had, in turn, been read out to Jordan's manager the next day, who laughed, said it all sounded great, thanks very much and how big would it be and would we like some pictures? And in it went, into the paper.

The same system was used for Abi Titmuss. There are scores of interviews of her in the vaults, sexily pouting about how she loves doing this and that, and being trussed up in silk, or stockings, or whatever. She didn't say a word of it. The journalists would invent a line or quote they wanted her to say, and it would be put to the agent who okayed it as long as there was a plug for the latest calendar or whatever. 'Oh, please,' I remember Abi sighing with despair on the phone one day, as I asked to her agree that she was, 'an angel in the courtroom and a whore in the bedroom.' 'I sound like such a tart if I say that. Do I have to?'

Of course, once all her sex tapes got leaked on the internet, we dropped all that and simply quoted her direct from the camera footage, but this is how it was done in the early days.

This is how most of the celebrity columns are done too. We even ran a weekly column with Jade as our resident TV critic at one point. But at least she was one of the hard-working ones, in that she'd ring us with pointers about what she was to 'write' that week. 'All right?' she'd said cheerfully on the phone, ''ere, can I have a pop at Kate Lawler again?'

One step down from the people quoted directly, are a shadowy army of 'friends', 'close friends', 'sources' and 'industry insiders', who also regularly pop up in tabloid papers with quotes. Let me explain who all these people are.

'A close friend' is usually the star themselves. They pass down all the information but ask not to be quoted. A 'friend' is often the star's agent or publicist. These people are on fifteen per cent of all the celebrity's income, need to keep them in the headlines, and tend to stick to the 'all publicity is good publicity' line – unless it's something *really* illegal – and are therefore usually quite keen to let stories run. Ring them with a story about their client and they tend to give you a quote confirming the whole lot, or least an indication of whether they were likely to sue if the piece goes in.

If they won't help, find out who the star's ex-agent, manager or PR is. Ring them instead. They are usually delighted to hear of any scandal and rarely miss an opportunity to bad-mouth their former cash cow. Anonymously, of course. They will also tend to furnish you with a little extra detail of any former misdemeanours which you may not have been aware of. I once rang someone hoping for a fairly innocuous quote on Anne Diamond from an industry figure who'd worked with her and ended up being taken out for lunch, where I was given a lengthy and highly entertaining breakdown of her living, eating and marital habits. I didn't even have to pick up the bill. All this was attributed to an 'industry insider'. Ex-lovers are good for this, too.

Read a piece that just quotes a 'source', and nine times out of ten it will have been simply been made up by a hack on deadline who's desperate to get to the pub.

Although general news is all about fact gathering, accuracy, taping and digging for information, Showbiz is, I discovered, mainly about inventing.

We'd have an annual 'Wing Commander' award at the Shaftas ceremony for the biggest 'flyer' we'd managed to get into print – in other words, the story that had been plucked out of thin air and safely brought to land in a paper with no legal comeback. Mostly it's harmless stuff designed to keep stars in the papers. Managers would ring in when a client was on the shortlist for, say, appearing on a reality show, or about to release a single and needed a boost to their profile. I would frequently be in on deals where we'd arrange for the star to be seen out with another star for a 'romance' rumour, or we would suggest a 'secret' visit to a wedding or jewellery shop to set an engagement rumour running; especially if one, or both, of the stars were secretly gay. Or, between the agent and the newspaper, we'd all agree to start a story about how they were on the verge of splitting up with someone, or quitting, or trying for a baby, or changing sex, or whatever. Anything to get them a page lead. Sometimes the celeb was in on it, but quite often the first they knew about it was when they saw it in the paper. I had one TV star come storming across to me once, demanding to know where the 'completely untrue' story about him I'd just printed in that day's paper had come from. 'Your PR gave us all a press briefing on it yesterday,' I told him.

Tabloid personas are created. It is an industry. People, well Jordan aside, do not go round mouthing tabloid-friendly soundbites about their personal lives on cue. Lines and angles are cooked up between newspapers, PRs and managers. We get a page lead. They get coverage. Everyone's happy. There's even a Shafta awards special known as the 'Princess Margaret Award', for the most ludicrous story to make it into print that year. It's named in honour of a story that once got printed decades ago, saying Princess Margaret was about to appear in *Crossroads*. Of course that was a load of tosh, but it filled a space, plugged a show and no one got hurt. Decades later, nothing much has changed.

So, this culture exists. But it exists primarily in the Showbiz sector. It's harmless enough, I suppose. Yes, it's hardly a noble fight to present readers with the truth, but it keeps the person in the headlines and it keeps them making their money. And the next week there'll be something else made up by someone else, filling another space somewhere else. And it is, as a reader, hugely enjoyable to read. Let's face it, we all love a bit of tabloid gossip, don't we? We all love to pore over people's lives. *It's all a game.*

But sometimes, just sometimes, it all goes a bit too far. I thought that over the years. Sometimes it's not a game any more. Like the day Brownfinger decided he'd start inventing a few new lines about Paula Yates. On the day of her funeral.

'It *is* true,' insisted Brownfinger, with an hour to go until deadline. 'It is. Print it. You won't get sued. Honest.'

'You're fucking making it up,' I snapped back. 'Just admit it.'

'I'm *not*,' said Brownfinger. 'She was definitely wearing a mink bikini in her coffin.'

I remember this day. It was a very long day. And one of the days that helped me fall out of love with journalism.

Brownfinger had left our paper but not the business at the time. Now he was working as a freelancer, basically flogging everything he could to anyone he could. Fleet Street looks after its own, so even if you get fired from one paper, all journalists tend to rally round, giving work to reporters until they can land another job elsewhere. Brownfinger would be back on another newsdesk, on another national newspaper, within months.

But today, Brownfinger was with the press pack covering Paula Yates's funeral. She was a big star. Her life was flawed – as all the most interesting lives are – and her death was clouded with controversy. It was a big story and on the day she was buried, the whole of Fleet Street was out to cover it. She would be front page news for every title.

As ever on these big media occasions, the desk tends to send dozens of reporters, assuming that the more men there are on the job, the more thorough the reporting will be. Unfortunately, all this really means is that one sucker does all the work. Whilst everyone else gets drunk.

As the most junior sucker there, I dropped Crump off at the pub and went off to the service.

'We'll come up with some colour for the piece,' Brownfinger and Crump had assured me as they headed to the bar. 'You get the basics.'

Paula Yates led a colourful life, which was reported on at every turn. The reports were no doubt, as ever, part fact, part fiction, but always lurid, always startling, always extremely readable.

But the funeral was different. For all the rumours that flew about in life, the truth was that she was leaving a young family without their mother. The funeral was a dignified, respectful affair.

I watched, just metres way, as the cars drove into the crematorium. On big stories where the picture will be a guaranteed front page, photographers can behave like absolute animals, desperate to get the image. But for once, Fleet Street behaved with a modicum of respect. As a photographer attempted to clamber onto the bonnet of a passing car to photograph Bob Geldof, who held a terrified Tiger Lily on his knee inside, he was yelled at by journalists and hauled away by furious staff photographers so the car could pass unhindered.

Outside the service, the journalists stood in silence. Funerals are never the nicest of jobs. The family arrives in tears and you're there, uninvited, recording the whole thing, feeling like an absolute leech. The family had hired PR men to hand out details of the service to the press pack and brief them. As we stood outside, we could hear a recording of Paula singing, playing out across the air. For a woman surrounded by scandal, it appeared the final chapter would, finally, be a peaceful one.

Except we'd reckoned without Brownfinger.

After three hours covering the service, I got the call from the newsdesk saying that Brownfinger had just filed some 'colour' and they were a bit unsure about it. Could I please check it out whilst I was there?

'He says Paula is being buried in a mink bikini,' said the News Editor.

My heart sank. How do you check out this one?

It's not unusual to find weird theories circulating in newspapers when a famous person dies. A dead person cannot sue. This is why, in what to any outsider must look startlingly insensitive, just hours after anyone of interest dies, reporters rake back through the vaults for any bits of gossip or tittle-tattle that they couldn't print when the person was alive for fear of a lawsuit. Crazy stories of various liaisons and follies tend to emerge. Theories about a hidden life. Legally speaking, Fleet Street can write anything it likes. But this was possibly a new low.

I went in search of Brownfinger. He was still in the bar with Crump. Who didn't appear to be able to see any more. 'It's kosher,' Brownfinger insisted. 'Everyone's going with it. I've got a really good source.' I pointed out that he was still in the same bar, at the same table, where I'd left him three hours ago. Had the source wandered, fortuitously, into the pub?

His hands fluttered in nervous denial. 'No. Really. I've got this amazing contact . . .' he said. 'I've talked to them. But I can't reveal my sources . . .'

I went back to the service. An hour of phone calls and furtive conversations with grieving family friends followed. Quite rightly, most looked at me in abject horror when I asked if any of them knew what the woman they were all crying for, and just seen cremated, had been wearing as she was carried into the crematorium? 'Who are you wearing?' questions are all very well on the red carpet, but being approached by a journalist, at a funeral, with an enquiry about coffin wear was another thing. I got a sea of shocked glares. And felt horrendous.

Meanwhile the News Editor came back. They'd drawn up the front page. They had word other titles on Fleet Street were going for it. It was an amazing line. Surely there was someone there I could ask?

I hung up and swore profusely, and at length, at both Brownfinger and the desk.

How do you ask this one? I know a deadline's a deadline, but the family were still in the service. I could hardly knock on the doors mid-wake and start making enquiries about mink bikinis to the congregation, could I?

So it was lucky my phone went at this point. With the funeral director. The name of his firm had been on the side of the hearse and I'd left several messages earlier on. He was fuming. I can hardly blame him. He told me they'd been with the family when they requested what outfit she was buried in. And it wasn't a bikini, it was her favourite dress. He was close to tears. 'Please. Can't you at least give her a bit of dignity in death and stop this one?' he said. 'Please?'

For me, this was the start of a period in tabloid newspapers where it began going wrong. It's easy to lose sight of the people involved. Safe in our little offices, where we never actually see the people we're writing about, the hunt is on to fill the paper. It's easy to simply approach each story with a cold, business eye. What will sell papers? What will make money? There is a feeling of invincibility in the newsroom, as it seeks out and prints each story, and if no one's there to check it, things can start getting out of control.

We almost went with the story, save for the fact that our News Editor was one of the old boys, who'd been in the game long enough to spot when a story is an absolute stinker; a flyer that just isn't worth the pain it's going to cause.

He got the story pulled, at great expense. The edition was delayed as it was re-written. We ended the day with The Editor seething.

The next morning I looked at the newsstands. Brownfinger had not given up, I saw. A rival paper had the front-page story: *Exclusive: Paula's exit in mink bikini.* On page one.

With full details. They'd said it was 'a white bikini from Jasper Conran'. And apparently they'd managed to find a family friend who they claimed had told them, 'What better way to make an entrance than to come through the Pearly Gates wearing a white mink bikini?'. I'd seen the reporters from that paper earlier in the day. They'd been in the bar with Brownfinger.

A legal letter arrived from the family shortly afterwards. And an apology and correction was printed in the newspaper.

There is a line between what is and what isn't acceptable, and on the day of Paula's funeral, it was crossed by the reporters on the job.

It wasn't only the likes of Brownfinger though. I think we often crossed it. Whether it was because of deadlines looming, desperation to keep the job, desperation to pay the rent. Or perhaps because when thousands of stories are churned out each week, it's easy to lose sight of the impact those stories have on the people involved. Instead your sole focus is on those white pages of a paper that are screaming to be filled.

This wasn't the only time we got it wrong. Sometimes we bullied people into confessions. Sometimes we goaded them. I know one woman who was called when she was on her way to an abortion clinic. Fleet Street has many good men. But occasionally, just occasionally, it doesn't know when to stop the story spinning. Occasionally, just occasionally, its good men behave like total tossers.

Speaking of which, I was never quite sure whether to admire or despise Brownfinger's explanation when called in front of The Editor to explain himself. It's an argument he still repeats to this day:

'Paula was wearing the bikini *under* the dress. Honest.'

I met Paula in life. She was a riot. She was causing mayhem and mystery right until the end. Fleet Street bickering at her graveside, ending the day in a hail of writs, front pages and furious editors.

She's someone who played the game like the best of us. Thrived off the publicity, sold the stories, colluded in the articles. Got how the whole crazy system worked. But in the end – for all the madness we make up during a person's life – a death, a tragedy, and a family's grief, is real.

15

BOLLOCKINGS FROM BRUCIE

And the Art of Apologising

Even though I successfully fought my way to a job in the tabloids, got to work on the very best titles, alongside the very best people in the job, I don't think I was a particularly good red-top hack. Actually, looking back, I was a pretty lousy one.

To be a good tabloid journalist you need to be ruthless. Get the story at all costs. Go in prepared to fight for your byline. I clung in there year after year. One day, around eight years after first walking through the office doors, I went for lunch with Robohack. He'd been promoted by now. He was being groomed for management. 'You know,' he said, 'I just don't think you're really cut out to be a tabloid journalist. I don't think you've got what it takes.'

At the time I took a renewed vow of hatred for him. How

dare he? I'd trained for this since I was a teenager, I'd spent years slogging away in national newspapers. I'd completely messed-up my life and put it on hold to go into the maddest situations. I'd had splashes. Great splashes. I'd been a success. I was furious. How dare he tell me I wasn't cut out for it?

But perhaps he was right. In fact I was only to survive another couple of years as a national newspaper reporter, before agreeing with him and resigning.

Right from the first day of training, my first day on the paper, I knew I wasn't a perfect tabloid hack. Because there were jobs out there that I didn't have the killer instinct for. I have to admit that, a few times over the years, there were jobs that I simply couldn't bring myself to do.

Death Knocks, for example. I hated these. Never did them. The idea is that you go and knock on the door of a mourning family, just after the death, and tell the family you are there to do 'a tribute' to their relative and try and get a sit down chat. The best time to do this, we are told during training, is just after the death or just after the funeral. Emotions will be high, the copy will be powerful, and the story will be good.

But I could never do it. About a year before Paula's death, I was sent to a doorstep shortly after the funeral of sports presenter Helen Rollason, who I'd met and interviewed a few times before. But when her daughter answered the door, I felt like the lowest of the low and couldn't say a word. Instead I awkwardly pushed some flowers at her, said they were a gift from the paper, burst into tears and turned on my grubby little heels and fled.

Of course, I told the desk, I'd stayed, cajoled, begged, and done all I could. Or they'd have sent me back.

I wasn't the only one to be useless at this. Many reporters, when ordered to ring grieving mothers in the hours after the death of their child, would merely sit there at their desks, repeatedly ringing their own home answering machines. As News Editors stood over them telling them to 'try again', they would fill up their home tapes with interview requests they knew would never be heard or granted. You have to have a particularly strong brass neck to stand there and try and get two pages out of a grieving mother. There were some questions that we just didn't want to be the ones to ask.

Having said that, there's plenty we did get up to. Not all of which was entirely moral.

Like the day I really upset Bruce Forsyth. Yes, I know, Brucie. Lovely, cuddly, fuzzy old Brucie. I still feel bad. My mum was absolutely livid when she heard.

Bruce Forsyth had invited me into his lovely palatial home for an interview. I'd admired his floor rugs, which were, I was delighted to report back home, really similar to the ones that my grandmother had bought off Chorley market not that long ago. His gorgeous wife Wilnelia made me tea and toast and we had a little chat in which Brucie talked about his autobiography. Brucie, who was employed by ITV at the time, gave a long overview of his life and showbiz career, then made a few throwaway remarks at the end saying he didn't like the new generation of TV presenters because they taunted their guests, that TV was choosing youth over experience and that TV chiefs should be careful about backing volatile stars like Michael Barrymore. He was also a bit fed-up of being shunted away on a little-watched mid-afternoon slot after several decades on prime time.

I wrote it up. It was all a bit star struck, to be honest. I'd grown up watching the *Generation Game* and just wrote a long dull article saying how fabulous he was and plugging his book. The Editor decided he didn't like it. It was all too boring. I didn't blame him. I'd even mentioned the carpet. It was spiked.

Until a month later, on a slow news day with a blank page to fill, when it was dug up from the vaults by a desperate Sub, who then proceeded to rewrite the lot. This time, it was a much racier read. It said that Forsyth had viciously 'slammed' his TV colleagues. And that he was an old 'whinger' and 'moaner'. And was attacking ITV chiefs and other rival stars. It was based on a grain of the original article, with a whole heap of top-spin and bile. And this time it made the cut.

Reading it in the paper the next day, I tried to work out what the best thing was to do about it all. It was entirely different from the piece that I'd written, and, unfortunately, entirely different to the piece that I'd sent over to Bruce and his agent for copy approval. At best, we'd totally gone against our word. At worst, they could sue. In the end – and I acknowledge this wasn't the brightest or bravest of decisions – I decided that the best thing to do was to pretend I hadn't seen it, and that it wasn't actually in a paper, and that four million copies hadn't just been sold, and do and say absolutely nothing. The approach had always worked with my parents, after all. So I folded the paper away and pretended it hadn't happened.

I carried on pretending it wasn't there for over a week, until his agent rang and asked what the hell we were playing at and why the hell I hadn't had the guts to ring him and let him know. 'Bruce,' he said, 'was devastated. We were waiting for you to call and apologise.'

Good grief. Devastating Brucie. My mum was furious. 'That wasn't a very nice story,' she said. 'Was it yours?'

'I know,' I mumbled guiltily. Come to think of it, throughout all the orgies, the fetish parties, the break-ins and the doorsteppings, I only ever got it in the neck once from home. And that was for upsetting Brucie.

There's a golden rule in journalism. If you're in the wrong, never, ever apologise. If you ring or write with an apology to anyone, it's an admission of guilt. They could tape you. Play it in court. Use it as evidence to sue you. Send a 'sorry' to anyone and you're basically inviting them to send you a writ and dictate how much they want writing on the cheque.

'Do *not* ring him,' instructed the News Editor. 'You can't.'

'*Ring him*,' ordered my mum.

Who would you listen to? Like I said, I wasn't a good tabloid journalist. I proved that by choosing who to listen to.

Wilnelia answered the phone. She sighed softly when I gave my name. I felt even lower. I'd upset Wilnelia too. Oh God. I was a truly evil human being. Then Brucie came on the phone.

I said sorry.

He accepted. In a quiet, gentlemanly way which made me feel even worse. He said he'd been upset. He said he'd been misquoted. It had been twisted. He said he'd trusted us. In comparison to bollockings from The Editor it was all completely tame. No broken bones. No football. And it was dreadful. Worse. I felt rotten. I'd have preferred the football over the guilt to be honest.

'Please get out of newspapers,' I remember he told me. 'It's a nasty game. They do nasty things. It'll turn you into a nasty person. Please get out.'

I hung up. Sat out in the fire escape where I'd been hiding whilst I made the call, out of earshot of the desk. I pondered what he'd said.

Then I went home, drank lots of wine and pondered some more. Yet another warning that I should get out the business. A man who'd survived seven decades in showbiz and bagged a Miss World as a wife had just given me life and career advice. But should I take it? Should I really just quit it all? How would I pay the rent? What would I do? And was it true? Was it really true? We weren't *that* bad were we? Or were we?

Well yes, I'd say we probably were. I certainly was that bad when it came to my private life. Oh yes, my love life was so appalling that by now I had progressed to attempting threesomes with my colleagues.

Mind you, I was bloody rubbish at that too.

My improbably unlucky evening started, as many did at this time, by drinking vodka. I was in the press room at the Brit Awards with a leading columnist who I better not name, and one other hack. The three of us, two girls and a man, were watching the succession of rock Gods take to the stage, hoovering our way through a litre of Smirnoff, and, occasionally, filing.

'I wish I'd been a pop starlet,' I sighed, as we all stared at Sarah Harding, who'd just been led into the press room. Ms Harding had been a godsend to tabloids ever since she appeared on *Pop Stars: The Rivals* and got into Girls Aloud. Before finding fame, she'd dated what I can only describe as a stream of utter shits. They all used to ring in with kiss-and-tells. For several months, Ms Harding's exes provided us with at least two pages a week of saucy detail on her. In fact her nickname amongst hacks was 'Miss Page 12 & 13'. Pages twelve and thirteen are the pages in the middle of the paper which tend to get chosen for double-page spreads of gorgeous young ladies in their underwear. They're within the first six pages of the newspaper that a punter may flick through whilst idling, deciding whether to buy the paper or not in the newsagents. If you've had a juicy splash, a bit of showbiz sauce, some moving human interest story and a picture of some young beauty in her knickers by that stage, the punter tends to pick it up.

Anyway, Miss Page 12/13 was up being interviewed and applauded by everyone for being fabulous and I was jealous. 'That's not a bad career choice,' I said to my fellow hacks. 'Being a pop starlet. You just rock and roll all day, sleep with each other and get up on stage to mass applause all night.'

We sat, drinking more vodka, and agreed Ms 12/13 had made a better career choice than us. Then stared at another starlet who came in, someone who was rumoured to be rather fond of threesomes.

'I've never had a threesome,' I moaned as I watched her. I think I'd had about a third of a bottle at this stage. 'I can't believe I'm this old and I've never had a threesome. My life is so dull. I would have had a threesome if I'd been a pop star-let. Journalism was the wrong career choice when it came to threesomes.' The three of us nodded. We would all have been neck deep in threesomes if we'd been pop starlets. On we drank. Some copy was possibly filed.

At some point, as the bar shut, we moved to a backstage aftershow party for more vodka, and, from there, we moved to a hotel. As daylight broke, the bartender said the bar was shutting. But we were still thirsty, we said. We were on expenses. We'd like to carry on.

'You're not guests,' the barman pointed out.

We brandished a credit card, bought another round of drinks and a hotel suite.

'We are now,' we replied.

'If anyone asks, we were drinking with the Osbournes and Jack was really thirsty,' we concurred. We ordered another round. Together with an extra Jack Daniel's for our mate Jack.

Then someone, and I think it was the male hack, but can't be sure, suggested that as we had a rock star suite, we should all go up to it and have a rock star threesome. And we all, me and the other two, decided this was a bloody good idea. It was the sort of thing the Osbournes would have suggested we did. The sort of thing we would have done if we were pop starlets.

We moved to the bedroom. Brilliant, I thought. I'm about to enter my Rampant Slut phase of Singledom. Realising, in a briefly sober moment, that I was, yet again, in woolly tights and old knickers, I retired to the bathroom, disrobed, show-ered, shaved two half legs and emerged. Wantonly. In towelling. It couldn't have been more than five minutes later. I was ready to be ravished.

I was too late. They'd moved to the bed. As I watched them on the white sheets being rock stars, I realised I had, once again, missed the deadline. They had started without me.

I sighed and retired, alone, to the far side of the bed, thinking I'd wait for a break in proceedings then try again. I fell asleep. No one woke me.

Dumped during a bloody threesome.

In the morning we all woke up with a start, slightly surprised to find so many of us under the duvet, then politely took turns to shower. He picked up the bill, which I guess was quite gentlemanly under the circumstances. But then, he was staff, so he was on expenses.

God. It was no wonder I wasn't married was it?

I screened my parents' calls that day.

16

CONFESSIONS OF A TABLOID HACK

And the Art of Being a Bastard

Crump brushed the contents of his top drawer into his briefcase.

'Could you pack the rest and send it to me?' he said. 'Mind the bottom drawer. I mean Rentokil were notified but . . .'

'What you doing?' I asked, horrified.

'Getting out,' he said. 'It is,' he added, as he swept his brown and blue asthma inhalers into his bag, 'a young man's game. I ain't getting the stories any more. Most of my contacts are dead or in rehab. I'm sick of the bollockings. They've offered me a pay off. And I'm out.

'It'll be all right,' he added at the sight of my stricken face. 'The missus will get to see me.'

'Missus?' I said, confused. He'd never mentioned a Missus

Crump before. Not even during the time we'd woken up together on a stake out in Ibiza.

'Yes, Mrs Crump. We've been married for fourteen years now. Time to start a family,' he continued. 'And I can't start one here. I can't even raise a smile at the end of the day.

'Maybe I'll spend my pay off on rehab. Or maybe I'll blow the whole lot and emigrate to a Tuscan vineyard. But it'll work out. It always does. Old hacks never die you know. They just go and make trouble elsewhere.'

He wandered over to Anne's desk, said goodbye, and swiped a few phials from her desk. She pretended not to notice.

'Oh,' he added, coming back. 'Forgot the bad news. Robohack. He's taking over my job. He's your boss now.'

And he dropped the phials into my hand, kissed me on the forehead, wished me luck and lurched out.

A lot of the old boys have been forced out of papers. These journalists, who had been on the papers for decades, may have been expensive to run, and may have a tendency to take a three-hour lunch, but what they did have was a heart. You could go to them with a query about what to do with a story, and, over a pint they would give you advice based on decades of knowledge. They were always right. A steadying hand on the tiller. I used to sit next to a wizened old boy who'd been a reporter for over forty years. He chain-smoked Bensons cig-arettes, coughed and spluttered all day and generally always sounded like he was on his last legs. But he was razor sharp. I'd occasionally catch him looking at my screen through the fug of his smokes and silently shaking his head at what I'd written, or tutting over The List, pre-Conference. His instinct always proved correct. Whenever the desk ignored his advice, a fax from Carter-Ruck was soon to follow.

These were the gentlemen journalists. They played by a set of rules. But a lot have gone now. Cutbacks or coffins. One of the two gets them. Journalism isn't the healthiest or steadiest of professions.

I think that as we've lost some of our gentlemen reporters, we've also lost some ethics. And I think that as the fame industry's changed, as reality TV culture has created overnight stars, we've created some monsters.

And by the time I left the tabloids, I wasn't sure who was the worst. Us or the people we wrote about.

I'll start with the journalists. Because we were pretty bad. By the end of my career I had seen some Very Bad Things. Some of them I did myself.

Robohack strode into the office with a flourish one day. Taking a bow and acknowledging applause as he passed the newsdesk. 'Quite a splash you've got there Robohack. How'd you get that one then?' he was asked.

It was, indeed, quite a splash. A touchingly detailed interview with a TV star's father, who was dying of cancer. It was strange, because repeated requests from the Showbiz desks across the country for an interview had been met with a refusal.

But Robohack didn't take refusals. He'd got the story by pitching up wearing his trusty white coat at the dying man's house. Presuming he was a doctor, his family let him inside and led him to the bedside. There the elderly man, and his

250

wife, proceeded to give every detail of his fight against terminal cancer. Robohack held his hand and gently asked about how their famous son was bearing up. A secret tape recorder captured the lot.

They didn't realise they were talking to a national newspaper journalist until the story ran on the front page.

He wasn't the only one to con his way into a story with a uniform. Honestly, some days in the office there were that many fancy dress outfits being put on it was like walking into an episode of *Mr Benn*.

I never did the old white coat stunt, but a lot of the things I got up to were equally as questionable. I have to confess to a few instances that could probably be filed under 'being a bit naughty'. By which I mean something that I probably wouldn't spend time in jail for if caught, but I had noticed that people who didn't work in tabloids had started to recoil whenever I mentioned what I was up to.

I had a nice backhander deal with child stars on red carpets for example. I'd hold out bank notes at their eye level as they passed, to tempt them over. Chesney from *Coronation Street* soon cottoned on that he was in for at least a tenner if he walked straight past the other reporters and gave an interview to me and me alone. Once word got round amongst the child stars it used to cost me a fortune at awards ceremonies.

And I'd break into celebrity weddings a lot. If a few of these people off the telly look back at their wedding album – at the happy crowd scenes as they come out of the church – they'll probably see me there, smiling and throwing confetti. The trick here – should you ever need to crash a B-list wedding – is to get there really, really early, before the best man, the vicar or, crucially, either of the wedding couple have turned up. Wear an unremarkable hat and a dull pastel outfit that won't attract any attention and then sort of mingle around, smiling vaguely at everyone. If you're out in public wearing something with feathers on, people always tend to believe you're a wedding guest and you get waved through most security cordons.

Hang out in a group and look vaguely friends with everyone and you'll be waved straight into the service, no questions asked. If ever anyone asked who I was, I'd smile and say I was a friend of the bride's 'from WeightWatchers'. Okay, maybe you could argue that it's immoral to have been there. But our view was always that if they'd chosen to flog their wedding to a magazine, it was fair game for us to have an invite too.

Mind you, other hacks would take it further. Crump gate-crashed a funeral once for a story. Then made the mistake of leaving his mobile phone in the crematorium. He had to nip back into the room and around the curtained-off coffin to get it, only to get stuck in the next funeral service which was filing in. He tried to leg it out the way he'd come in, but his route was blocked by another incoming coffin and grieving family.

'Ended up stuck in there singing *The Lord is My Shepherd* all afternoon and pretending to cry as this bloke glared at me, wondering who this strange man in a suit was, crying at his wife's funeral,' he complained as he got back to the office four hours later. 'Quite moving service though.'

And some of the other things I did were a bit underhand. I once attempted to scale a six-foot-high fence, trying to get

252

Ulrika's autobiography from a printing press, and would happily have stolen a copy had I not clocked the crowd of security men and CCTV watching me. And I did own a natty waitress outfit, and even went on a course to learn silver service skills. At showbiz ceremonies where press were barred, you'd simply apply for a job as a waitress or barman, or failing that, go to the back and sneak in carrying a tray of champagne. I remember the night Della Bovey turned up at a party a few days after being ditched by Grant Bovey, who'd run off with Anthea Turner. I'd snuck in as staff and as soon as Della entered the room, I made a beeline for her with my silver tray. I practically collided with two other waiters and, as I looked at them in horror, we realised all three of us were hacks working undercover.

There were loads of sneaky tricks. I'd often leave an interview after ten minutes, pretending to need a loo break and making a big point of switching off a tape recorder which was placed on top of the table. But I'd have another tape recorder running in my handbag, which was placed strategically under the table and would continue to run and record private conversations when I went out the room. It's a great way of getting an unexpected exclusive as the subject turned to their PR/lover/rentboy and said, 'God, I hope she doesn't know about . . .'

So was I a bad journalist? Possibly. Unethical? Probably. Did some of this behaviour go against the spirit of the press code of practice, that insists on the 'highest professional standards' and a promise not to publish, 'inaccurate, misleading or distorted information'? Most definitely. But I wasn't nearly the worst.

Basically, a tabloid hack can get any information they want. On anyone. There are ways and means. Newspapers used Fixers. Blaggers. There were people you could call. One source was christened Benji the Binman, because he regularly rifled through the rubbish of the rich, famous and infamous and sold the contents of their bins to newspapers for cash. Journalists would pose as cleaners and go raking round rival newsrooms in bins and printers for stories.

There was one freelancer who was known for being able to pull people's medical records – no one quite knew how he did it. But rumour had it he posed as a GP, rang the person's doctor and said he was taking over their treatment, or attending an emergency case with them, and needed their records to be faxed over. The same guy had shadowy contacts within mobile phone firms, who could hand over phone records for anyone you wanted – a useful way of seeing if two people who were alleged to be having an affair were engaging in long late-night chats together. For the record, should you be a high profile person who is engaging in an illicit affair, I would recommend you purchase two of those Pay As You Go phones, and do your booty calls on those. Hacks can't trace them.

This wasn't the only trick you could pull with a mobile phone. Dial any mobile number, enter one of a series of numerical codes and you can listen to all the voice messages which have been stored on the phone. This method hit the headlines when a journalist was sent to jail for listening into private messages to get stories on the royals. Oddly, although not one single journalist in the UK will ever admit to getting stories by this method, and everyone agrees it's a terrible, immoral thing to do, every journalist who has ever worked on any tabloid will know exactly how to do it and which codes you use. Incidentally, if you want to stop journalists hacking in, you simply set up a four digit PIN number on your account; the codes won't work any more and no one can hack in. Don't use the year you were born though. That's the first four-number PIN code hacks try.

It wasn't just the Royals who were targeted. One international megastar got so fed up with her phone being hacked into by journalists that she ended up leaving a voicemail which ended, 'And will you bloody journalists stop hacking into my fucking voice messages'. I heard it playing into the air one morning as I arrived at the office. Crump was looking devastated as he listened and muttering, 'Damn it. Guess that little source is busted then.' Still, he wasn't the worst. One hack used this method so often to get so many stories, without ever moving from his desk, that he was nicknamed The Olympic Flame. He never went out.

Fleet Street has cleaned up its act a lot, but I don't think it will ever totally let go of its bad ways. Hacks are pushed by deadlines, pushed to fill the paper, pressured as they face a relentless daily push to deliver, whilst all the time being challenged by younger, cheaper shifters coming up through the ranks who are desperate to steal their jobs. On newspapers you not only compete against the rest of Fleet Street, but bosses would frequently put a desperate young journalist and an older staffer on the same story and set them in competition against each other. Add to that the constant threat of redundancy as circulations fall and staffing levels decrease each year, so newspapers can survive. No excuse for the old Dark Arts, as we used to call them, but as it gets harder and harder to survive, it perhaps goes some way to explaining why these practices persist.

There are many amazing journalists on many amazing papers, but across all titles are a sprinkling of chancers and risk-takers, those that go outside the boundaries of what's quite morally right. Those who are evilly brilliant and will do anything to get that byline. Those are the best, or arguably the worst, in Fleet Street.

Tabloid hacks do not tend to be nice people. Not in office hours. They have to get the story. They have to save their job. If they don't do it, someone else in the industry will. The other person will get the story and the glory. You will get your P45.

Still, if you think the stuff we do is bad, it's nothing compared to what the celebrities themselves got up to.

17

CELEBRITIES BEHAVING BADLY

And the Art of Knowing When to Quit

People often wonder how hacks find out so much about the private lives of the rich and famous. The answer is that, fairly often, the celebrities do their damndest to help fill the spaces themselves.

'My wife needs sectioning.' It was 3 am in the morning and the husband of a household name was on the phone.

For months now stories about a high-profile couple had been printed in the paper. Although, in public, they were all smiles and holding hands, these stories of rows and fights kept surfacing and, although the pair repeatedly and publicly denied any problems in their marriage, I knew they would never make a legal complaint about any of the stories which were all running under my byline.

The reason why I knew this, was that they were leaking the

stories themselves. Each was secretly selling stories about the other. She'd ring late one night and say he was cheating on her. He'd ring and say she was drinking too much. The next week there was a claim of domestic violence. The next time a call to claim insanity. I ran the vast majority of it and quoted each of them as a 'source close to' the couple. And then carefully added in the denial that was issued from their furious agent.

The calls came so often that I'd taken to sleeping with my mobile phone rigged up to a tape recorder at night. That way I could just pick it up, say 'hello' and press 'record' whilst they each ranted on in turn into the early hours. Unhappy times for them, but happy days for me. I could collect a page lead in my sleep with a cast-iron source for each, without ever having to switch on the light or leave my pillow.

They weren't the only ones selling themselves. One star used to ring us the second she ever got a date. She would choose a location that she knew would be overlooked by a handy balcony, field or hotel for the snapper to sit in. The unsuspecting beau would pitch up, and, as soon as she saw the lens was in place, the starlet would whip off her top and pounce on her – often completely bewildered – date. The bit that made us laugh was that once she was sure we'd had a chance to snap her, she would 'spot' us and then start screaming and pointing at the lens and go running over to berate the 'scum' for photographing such an 'intimate moment'. The poor man would inevitably be trailing behind her, trying to placate his 'distraught' date. She'd get picture approval plus thousands in cash in brown envelopes from us over the years. She's still at it now.

It's a similar tale behind all those pages of 'candid' beach shots of gorgeous, pouting bikini-clad babes who used to be in *Big Brother* or a soap. The dear girls used to ring us directly to say where they were going on holiday, and pre-arrange to be on a certain beach, at a certain time, where they'd emerge, in full make-up, like a goddess from the waves, bikini top having 'accidentally' slipped. These shots all tended to operate on a 50/50 deal between them and the local freelance photographer. The snapper flogs the pictures around the globe and hands over half the profits to the girl. The girls would make thousands. They'd get double for topless. I'm not knocking this, by the way. In fact I used to introduce the girls to the snappers and suggest they did it. My cut of the deal was that I got first option to buy in the picture set for the paper.

The problem is, that as more of these manufactured stars emerge with each new TV show, the stories must get ever bigger, ever more dramatic to get into print and compete. And the stars get ever more desperate and start faking big events to create a steady stream of stories.

Some of them are ludicrous. Like the household name who once negotiated a £50,000 deal for the story of his 'engagement' to a ravishing TV presenter in a top glossy magazine. The only tiny flaw was that he never got round to telling the TV presenter about it, before he struck the deal. After having only ever met him once, for coffee, in a crowded room, she was slightly bewildered when he rang up to beg her, 'Oh, please. Let's be engaged. Oh, go on. We'll go 50/50 on the deal. There'll be nice pictures. And there's bound to be TV work on top.' She said no.

Or the TV star who literally sat in the cab, as his pregnant girlfriend went in for a scan. Behind her back he was negotiating a cash deal for the news of 'whether it was a boy or a girl' to the hack on the phone. Secretly selling the pics of his first-born whilst the child was still in the womb.

Some of them were crazy. Like the star who seriously considered faking a pregnancy, offering to wear an ever-growing fake baby bump. Quite how she thought she was going to keep on faking it past the nine month mark, I'm not sure.

And some of them are just laughable. Like the TV star who was giving a heart-rending interview about, 'beating cocaine addiction'. All very moving, was it not for the fact that en route to the studios for the photographs he'd sneezed over the back of the car seats. Which were instantly covered in a fine white powder. 'Shall we go on?' he was asked, as the powdery evidence dripped down the leather.

But we did go on. We went on printing them. Day after day. Week after week, deals were struck as the pages had to be filled.

It took me a decade to realise that my appalling love life may possibly be related to my career choice. Okay, I was slow on the uptake, but as you've probably gathered by now, I never have been that bright where relationships are concerned. As previously demonstrated, I literally could not pull at an orgy.

People talk of being married to the job. Working on a newspaper is like having a fabulous yet demanding, petulant and unfaithful lover. You must work twenty-four hours a day to cater to the most outrageous and improbable of demands, whilst knowing all along that in the end you'll probably get dropped for someone younger and more willing. It must be like dating Tiger Woods rolled into Russell Brand rolled into Hugh Hefner. By my last year in the job, I was utterly knackered and getting thoroughly sick of its behaviour.

I remember my final doorstep. I'd been sent on a story that a *Holby City* actor was in a coma, fighting for life after a beating. I turned up at the actor's house, hoping for a chat with friends or relatives and was somewhat surprised to see the actor himself, Jeremy Edwards, jogging towards me. He was even more surprised at my opening question, and offered a rather startled quote to the effect that he was definitely vertical and definitely in the land of the living and had been all day. He even let me touch him to check he wasn't a ghost. I thought I'd been fairly thorough.

'Oh just fucking stand it up,' snarled Robohack, as I returned empty-handed to the office. 'It's a basic story. Can you do this fucking job or not?'

The truth is that the answer was increasingly becoming, probably not.

I remember being pulled once, mid-tooth extraction, from the dental surgery to attend a newspaper 'emergency' and sitting, blood dripping onto the keyboard, only to receive a bollocking from Robohack because I couldn't talk through the anaesthetic that had frozen my face. I did discover an up-side though, which was that my dentist would prescribe a course of valium after any surgery. Unfortunately, over the years, as I ran out of wisdom teeth to extract, the realisation dawned that if I was viewing the inability to go through major root-canal surgery as a minus point in life, then the thrill of the job may just be wearing off.

A big story hitting a newsroom is like a moment of electricity. There's a second of silence as the news comes in, before the explosion and the race, the hunt to get to the story first. One Features Editor used to take it to extremes, a wild manic fire in his eyes as he screamed, 'Get them! Get them!' to launch the chase. And for years I'd happily run. I would chase anything, *anything*, until the end of the day – mythical creatures, wild goose stories, leads, hunches, whims or shaggy dog tales. But you can't do it forever.

Journalism is great, but like I say it's a demanding lover. To appease it, you neglect your own life. I struggled to make weddings, anniversaries, christenings, to be with friends and family when they needed me. I remember crying in a car park somewhere in Elstree, stuck waiting for a press conference, wondering if I'd make it to a dying and much-loved relative's bedside in time. And you start to question if it is worth it.

The job does take over your life. For years, I'd only half listen to real friends crying about their real-life dramas, half my mind on some showbiz stranger and how I'd get them to talk about their, often imaginary, dramas in print. For if you don't give it that amount of dedication, you'll be forced out. Someone younger, better, keener will come along and take your job. You're only as good as your last byline.

And so, slowly, slowly, I realised I had fallen out of love with the job.

I'd been offered a job on the desk, a chance to climb up the tabloid food chain, but refused. For me, it was always the thrill of the chase that had appealed. But in the end the chase left me. As Crump said, journalism, reporting, is a young person's game. It needs a boundless energy, the ability to wordlessly and happily accept and serve the whims of a screaming boss, and the youth to think that the rest of your life can be put on hold to get this stuff. Because it matters.

Because you've plenty of time to worry about things like babies and husbands later. When you're older. When you're a grown up.

Except that, after ten long years, I started realising I didn't have plenty of time any more. I was thirty-five and I had spent so long chasing after other people's lives, I didn't have one of my own.

At every wedding I attended now, I'd start wondering if I'd ever get there myself. Wonder if I too shouldn't do something a bit more wholesome with my life, that would merit applause in churches?

Just as with my day with The Hoff, the old mask slipped. Just as with the day with the rave-demanding toyboy lover, I started to realise I was too old for this. And just as with TBOTT, I'd feel grubby in the morning when I looked back on what I'd done the night before.

They teach you the 'six ws' in journalism training to help you collate all the facts. The Who, What, Where, Why, When and hoW. Who is the story about, what did they do, where did it happen, why should we care, when did it happen and how?

And now, to this, I added a seventh. *What* am I doing? *What the fuck am I doing with my life?*

The next Christmas marked my tenth year since walking into a national newspaper office.

I'd travelled home and once more spent Christmas Eve cross-eyed and craving nicotine in a single bed. Ten years and I had not moved on, not succeeded at all since the day I left home. What had I been doing for the last decade? I'd had 120 pay cheques. What exactly had I got to show for it?

The single bed was a silent, two-foot-wide, lonely rebuke at my life. 'Come home,' it scolded me each year. 'Come home, and start again. Stop messing about pretending you're a grown up. You haven't changed. Nothing's changed. You've failed.'

I took the journey by train, just like I'd done all those years ago and I stared at the gardens of the houses that lined the train tracks. Thousands of windows. Thousands of windows with people living behind them. People with mortgages, pensions, families, with kids' toys in driveways. With glorious gardens that could only be achieved by quiet nights in with adoring other halves, watching *Gardener's World* together. Behind each window lived people who, unlike me, had somehow managed to figure it all out. I had no husband, no child, no mortgage. Not even a goldfish.

As I lay there that Christmas, it occurred to me that I was the first generation ever in my family to end up like this. To be hurtling towards forty with nothing to show for it. To spend the passing of each year alone in my childhood bed. Four million years of the miracle of evolution, and, after all that effort, all we had ended up with was me. A tabloid hack. Someone who couldn't get a boyfriend. Even when she went speed dating.

Homo Sapiens. Completus Failus.

And as a woman, whose career was about putting some

unsavoury facts down on paper, I began to realise there was one fact I had to come to terms with. As long as my life centred around this mad, bad world of the tabloid journalist, it was never going to change.

Another ten years from now I'd be chasing someone else. Filming someone else. Stalking someone else. Banging on doors and shouting improbable questions to someone else. Same old shit. Just a different cast.

I returned, post-Christmas, to work, and breathed in a pre-noon vodka and Silk Cut in the pub. I watched the shifters who were younger and thinner and shinier than me. The shifters who really wanted it, the shifters who'd do anything to get into tabloids. The shifters who were desperate for me, this booze-soaked old fart, to quit so they could get on with it, get my staff position and get an expense account. The shifters who had no bloody idea what they were begging to get into.

And I knew they'd love it. The twisting, the turning, the top-spinning. The ten impossible requests before breakfast. The hurtling of the day into fresh sex, scandal and celebrity. The mad, mad things that hacks do all day to fill that space. They'd love it because that's the only way through the job. To love it. And I knew I just couldn't do it any more. Because I didn't love it any more.

So I did what I probably should have done a decade ago. I rang home. I spoke to my parents. I asked for advice.

Parents are good at these things you know.

The next day I wrote my last two hundred words. And head-lined it 'Resignation'.

The morning after I left, I checked into a spa. I detoxed, I thought pure thoughts, I ate vegetables and I sipped pure water. I stopped smoking. I started yoga. I cancelled the papers, and I read Deepak Chopra. And I was pure and I was good.

And twelve hours later I thought, oh bollocks, I'm bored now. What am I going to do with the rest of my life?

And this bloody Deepak Chopra chap. He really ought to use shorter sentences. He'd never make it as a tabloid hack.

18

PUTTING THE PAPER TO BED

And the Art of Surviving After Tabloids

A year after quitting, I was at a bar at an awards ceremony. Although I'd quit tabloids I had ensured I stayed
friends with enough well-placed contacts to ensure the
free-bar aftershow party invites kept coming. It was bad
enough losing expenses. I made sure I clung onto a few
perks. A man was standing in the queue for the bar and
stopped me.

'Aren't you a tabloid journalist?' he asked. 'I think I've
seen your photograph in the paper?'

'No,' I said, signalling to the barman for another glass.
'Not any more. I've quit. Quit, quit, quit. Tabloid papers are
nothing to do with me. No matter what you may read, what
you may ever have read, it has nothing to do with me any
more.'

'Oh no,' he said. 'I never read any of your stuff I'm afraid. I just flicked straight to the back and the Sport section. What was it you wrote about anyway?'

It turned out there was a life post-newspapers. It was in TV. I got myself a lovely job in daytime TV as a reporter. I was standing on the red carpet with a microphone one day when Bruce Forsyth came into view, the crowd screaming his name.

Just as he'd predicted in the interview we never ran, he had the potential to be an A-List primetime star. Brucie was now the main presenter on the BBC's biggest hit for years, *Strictly Come Dancing*. The nation had fallen in love with him all over again.

Would Mr Forsyth, said a PR on the red carpet, please do a quick interview with me. With me and a rival TV show?

Bruce locked eyes with me.

He smiled.

He did the interview. It was a great interview. He was witty, funny, charming. He talked of his fellow stars. He gave great quotes about the knighthood the public was clamouring for him to be given. It was professional, sharp, front-page material.

And it was all peppered with quotes about how much he enjoyed the other reporter's rival show. So it was all, for me, completely unusable.

At the end he smiled politely, and walked off.

Doddery that man is not.

I miss the papers I worked for. I miss the newsrooms. I worked for some amazing people. Incidentally, in case you're still thinking of going into all this, don't worry. Do it. You'll enjoy it.

A lot of the tossers have been fired now. Not all mind, but it's better than it was. And there are still some wonderful old hacks out there who make the job a joy and a delight. They have the same excitement, the same love for the job as they did the day they first joined decades ago. If you join, look for these old boys, get them to take you under their wing and teach you how to do it properly.

Oh. And find yourself a lover before you go in, because trust me, you won't ever find a decent one once you're in there.

The only people who will ever understand the mad things you do all day are other journalists. And they're as bad as I was. You don't ever want to date one of them.

I haven't named the papers I was at when all these events took place. This is because although pretty much all the journalists were mad, drunken, immoral, sex-crazed chancers, deep down I love every double-crossing, slippery, two-faced little one of them. They're all still out there. All still working. Still surviving. I still love the tabloid press. I love its spirit and the thrill of what gossip lies in its pages. I read all the tabloid papers and I still see my ex-colleagues' names proudly emblazoned over words like 'torrid romp' and 'drug shame', and I smile. They're still churning out that copy, filling that space, day after day. Doing that is hard enough for them without them all being hauled off to see policemen, divorce lawyers, psychiatrists and people from Carter-Ruck to have to explain themselves because of something I wrote.

Besides, I don't blame them for doing what they did.

*

As a tabloid girl you will find yourself in the oddest positions, doing the oddest things. You will have to lie, scheme, cheat, secretly tape, con and beg to get the stories. You must crash weddings, funerals and lives and try not to crash and burn yourself in the process.

It's all in a day's work and sometimes I loved it, sometimes I hated it, but I lived it. It's a while since I left now. Not much has changed though. The Royal desk are still resplendent in pastels, the female columnists never get any older, the Showbiz reporters continue to be drunk, Investigations continue to put their lives on the line and yet Madonna, in her knickers, still gets on the front page.

Post-tabloids, I managed to change though. Just a little bit anyway.

Away from the tabloids, I finally cracked it. I am, finally, a 'we'.

The man from the bar, the one that only ever flicked through my tabloid bits on his way to Sport, called. I kept quiet about the orgies until date six. He carried on seeing me. He let me meet his mother.

So I finally got myself a Plus One in life. I've got a garden. I've got a mortgage. I've got *Gardener's World* on Sky Plus. I may even watch it one day.

Mum rang last week. I'm cracking on towards forty now. But I think they have finally started to hope. Finally, it seems, they believe I may have grown up. They're coming to mine for Christmas. I think I have finally spent my last night in my childhood bed.

My old flatmate got in touch last week, too. The smug one.

The one that would kick a trail of adoring men and Nigella nutmeg fumes into my stricken lovelorn face. The one who went to Clapham to get married.

'Fancy a drink?' she texted. 'I'm single again. Guessing you are too, hey? Let's go out on the pull!'

I stared at the text for half an hour.

Then wrote back.

'Would love to. But I'm frantically busy. Planning my wedding!'

Okay, so the man hasn't actually proposed yet, but the smug bitch asked for it. Sometimes in life you need a little bit of top-spin.

I pressed 'Send'.

Fuck the facts, I thought, *and just file.*

ACKNOWLEDGEMENTS

Thank you to the brilliant Antonia Hodgson at Little, Brown. She was the first person to say, 'Did you *really* do all that? Have you ever thought of writing a book about it?' Her wonderful guidance is issued over cream cakes at The Wolseley and always gratefully received. I've loved writing this and am thankful for having someone so talented believe in me.

She is ably assisted by the gorgeous team at Little, Brown, particularly by Hannah Boursnell who painstakingly edited the copy – pointing out the inaccurate, the improbable and the unprovable. Thank you to Marie Hrynczak in production, Hannah Clarke in design and Hannah Torjussen in publicity. To the book's lawyer, Meryl Evans, I am terribly sorry. You've had more detail on Dean Gaffney than a women should know in her lifetime.

The aptly named Gordon Wise from Curtis Brown continues to prove he has a brain the size of a planet and I am immensely proud and grateful to have him as my literary agent. And for his sage advice when he receives emails headed: 'Now. Do you think this chapter makes me look like a slut?' Thanks for backing me.

To my parents, who supported me and my ridiculous newspaper job from day one. As previously discussed, I would be grateful if you only read this page. There are things I believe you should never know about your daughter. Yes. That's it for you I'm afraid. Close the book now.

Leaving a reporting career does leave you with a huge void in your life, so I am grateful to Shu Richmond, TV executive and all round good egg, for coming to the rescue and starting my TV career by employing me over at ITV. And to Rebekah Wade, for the (sort of) compliment of pointing out that my love life was so appalling she'd like to make it a column in the *Sun*. You're both great editors and an inspiration to work for.

Thanks to Phil, Fern and all the gorgeous presenting and production team over at *This Morning* for being so welcoming. Particularly on days when probably the last person you wanted to see at breakfast was a red-top hack.

It is over twenty years ago now that I first knocked on the door of my local newspaper, the *Blackburn Citizen*, to see if anyone there would take me out for a drink and tell me how to get into the business. Harold Heys and Brian Caven took me under their wing for work experience, taught me how to write and taught me how to sup. It was Harold who told me to get on a train to London and, 'kick a few doors down and demand they let you work in Fleet Street.' Both great journalists, and I owe my career to them. Brian sadly isn't with us any more, but you can catch Harold sometimes at the excellent www.gentlemenranters.com. Talking of gentlemen, those whose doors I kicked included Hugh Whittow, David Wooding, and Gary Thompson. Good men all. Thanks

ACKNOWLEDGEMENTS

for employing me. When I write of the good bosses I had, I mean you.

Finally, thank you to Bruce Davidson. I still can't quite believe my luck that I found you. Thank you for all the cloud-busting, darling.